PRENTICE HALL
LITERATURE

PENGUIN  EDITION

Teaching Resources

Unit 2
Short Stories

Grade Nine

PEARSON

Prentice
Hall

Upper Saddle River, New Jersey
Boston, Massachusetts

ISBN 0-13-1340202-9

1 2 3 4 5 6 7 8 9 10   09 08 07 06 05

Contents

Part 1 Make Inferences

"The Jade Peony" by Wayson Choy

"American History" by Judith Ortiz Cofer

"The Most Dangerous Game" by Richard Connell

Part 2 Cause and Effect

"The Invalid's Story" by Mark Twain

"The Scarlet Ibis" by James Hurst
"The Golden Kite, the Silver Wind" by Ray Bradbury

Vocabulary Warm-up Word Lists

Study these words from "The Jade Peony." Then, complete the activities.

Word List A

appropriate [uh PROH pree uht] *adj.* proper; right for the purpose
The scary movie wasn't <u>appropriate</u> for preschool children.

conveyed [kuhn VAYD] *v.* made known; communicated
She <u>conveyed</u> her agreement by nodding her head.

diagnosed [DY uhg nohst] *v.* analyzed; identified a medical condition
Have you already <u>diagnosed</u> the problem with my computer?

elaborate [i LAB uhr it] *adj.* carefully worked out; complicated
It took many months to work out their <u>elaborate</u> wedding plans.

resisted [ri ZIST id] *v.* opposed; worked against
Although we <u>resisted</u> making the change, we finally gave in.

revealed [ri VEELD] *v.* showed; made known
Their careful investigation <u>revealed</u> startling new evidence.

undisturbed [uhn dis TERBD] *adj.* not bothered; not interrupted
The well-concealed tomb was left <u>undisturbed</u> for thousands of years.

wondrous [WUHN druhs] *adj.* wonderful
The vista point offered a <u>wondrous</u> view of the Grand Canyon.

Word List B

ancestral [an SES truhl] *adj.* inherited from ancestors
The <u>ancestral</u> coat of arms of the Chávez family includes five keys.

countless [KOWNT lis] *adj.* too many to count
Josh seemed to have <u>countless</u> excuses for not doing his homework.

deftly [DEFT lee] *adv.* skillfully, in a sure and easy way
The chef <u>deftly</u> chopped the vegetables into perfect cubes.

exasperation [eg zas puh RAY shun] *n.* irritation or annoyance
The annoyed expression on her face betrayed her <u>exasperation</u>.

fragments [FRAG ments] *n.* broken pieces
<u>Fragments</u> of glass covered the floor beneath the broken window.

perplexed [pur PLEKST] *adj.* puzzled; confused
He was <u>perplexed</u> by the sudden change in plans.

somber [SAHM ber] *adj.* solemn; gloomy
We were in a <u>somber</u> mood after hearing the bad news.

vividly [VIV id lee] *adv.* in a lively manner; clearly
I remember my first day of school as <u>vividly</u> as if it were yesterday.

"The Jade Peony" by Wayson Choy
Vocabulary Warm-up Exercises

Exercise A *Fill in the blanks using each word from Word List A only once.*

Last year, my Uncle Bob was [1] _____ with arthritis. At first, he kept his condition secret and [2] _____ it to no one. When his daughter found out, my stubborn uncle [3] _____ her efforts to help him. He asked not to be bothered. He just wanted to be left [4] _____. After many complex, [5] _____ conversations, my cousin finally [6] _____ to him the importance of seeking medical treatment. The doctors prescribed medications that were [7] _____ for treating my uncle's condition. Thanks to those [8] _____ pills, Uncle Bob is now able to dance again for the first time in years!

Exercise B *Find a synonym for each word in Word List B. Use each synonym in a sentence that makes the meaning of the word clear. (Hint: You may use a thesaurus to look for synonyms.)*

Example: Vocabulary word: <u>ancestral</u>   synonym: *familial*
   While visiting our <u>familial</u> homeland, we saw the house my great-grandfather grew up in.

1. <u>countless</u>   synonym: _____
_____

2. <u>deftly</u>   synonym: _____
_____

3. <u>exasperation</u>   synonym: _____
_____

4. <u>fragments</u>   synonym: _____
_____

5. <u>perplexed</u>   synonym: _____
_____

6. <u>somber</u>   synonym: _____
_____

7. <u>vividly</u>   synonym: _____
_____

"The Jade Peony" by Wayson Choy
Reading Warm-up A

Read the following passage. Pay special attention to the underlined words. Then, read it again, and complete the activities. Use a separate sheet of paper for your written answers.

I suppose I was always Grandfather's favorite.

Whenever he needed help expressing himself in English, I was the one he would turn to for help. Please understand that English was my only language. I usually had no more idea of what Grandfather was trying to say than anyone else did. Sometimes he <u>conveyed</u> his message to me through a series of grunting noises and <u>elaborate</u> hand gestures. I would then guess at his meaning. He would shake his head up and down to indicate whether my guess was correct. We were never really sure if shaking his head up and down meant *yes* or *no* to Grandfather, but sooner or later we would come to some sort of agreement about what he was trying to say.

When Grandfather complained, which was just about all the time, it was I who <u>diagnosed</u> his complaint. Occasionally, Grandfather <u>revealed</u> the source of his irritation to me directly. More often than not, though, I would have to guess what was bothering him. If others tried to help, he <u>resisted</u> their efforts by refusing to speak a word of English. Eventually, he would describe his problem to me, and I would suggest an <u>appropriate</u> solution. Sometimes I wondered if all his complaining was just an excuse to spend more time with me.

The only thing that consistently stopped Grandfather from complaining was the television. Left <u>undisturbed</u> on the sofa, Grandfather would spend hours staring at whatever images flickered across the screen. He didn't seem to care what was on or what language was being spoken. It was a <u>wondrous</u> sight to behold that cranky old man sitting quietly for hours.

Sometimes, after I finished my homework, I would sit at Grandfather's side for an hour or two and watch television with him. His eyes never left the screen, but, after about twenty minutes, his surprisingly strong hand would reach out and gently squeeze my shoulder. As best as I can remember, those were the only times I ever saw Grandfather smile.

1. Underline the words that tell how Grandfather <u>conveyed</u> his message. Then, write what *conveyed* means.

2. Circle the words that tell what Grandfather expressed with <u>elaborate</u> hand gestures. Describe how they might have been *elaborate*.

3. Circle the words that tell what the narrator <u>diagnosed</u>. What else can be *diagnosed*?

4. Underline the words that tell what Grandfather <u>revealed</u>. What things do you think he might have *revealed*?

5. Underline the words that tell how Grandfather <u>resisted</u> other people's help. Why do you think he *resisted*?

6. Circle the words that tell for what the narrator suggested an <u>appropriate</u> solution. Then, tell what *appropriate* means.

7. Underline the words that tell what Grandfather stared at if left <u>undisturbed</u>. What do you like to do when left *undisturbed*?

8. Underline the words that tell what the narrator describes as a <u>wondrous</u> sight. What *wondrous* sight have you beheld at home?

"The Jade Peony" by Wayson Choy
Reading Warm-up B

Read the following passage. Pay special attention to the underlined words. Then, read it again, and complete the activities. Use a separate sheet of paper for your written answers.

The first Chinese immigrants came to Canada around the end of the 18th century. The first great wave of immigrants did not arrive until the mid-1800s, however. Countless men, women, and children fled from Hong Kong during the Opium Wars. They sought to escape poverty and political unrest. The gold rush of 1858 brought even more Chinese to British Columbia. Unlike the European immigrants who came to start a new life, most of the Chinese who came to Canada intended to return to their ancestral homeland some day.

In the 1880s, cheap labor was needed to build the new Canadian Pacific Railroad. More than 5,000 Chinese were recruited from China and another 7,000 from California. The Chinese were excellent workers who deftly performed whatever tasks were required of them. First with exasperation, then with despair, they realized that their employers had little concern for their comfort or safety. Chinese workers were housed in flimsy canvas tents. Many were killed each night by falling rocks. Many more were killed every day in explosions after being struck by flying rock fragments. The mood of the workers grew somber. They were also perplexed to discover that non-Chinese workers were earning five times as much for their labor! In addition, the Chinese worked on the most dangerous sections of the railroad. Many died on the 300 miles of track that passed through the Rocky Mountains. Those who lived to tell about their experience vividly recalled the long days of backbreaking labor that was the plight of the Chinese railroad workers.

By the end of 1881, fewer than 1,500 of the original 5,000 workers from China were still alive. Taking the deaths in stride, the company promptly imported thousands more to take their place. Many more would die before the railroad was completed in 1885. With the railroad completed, the Canadian government immediately passed a series of laws designed to keep additional Chinese immigrants from entering the country.

1. Why is countless a good term to describe the "great wave of immigrants"? What else might you describe as *countless*?

2. In your own words, tell which relatives lived in the ancestral homeland of the Chinese. Write a sentence about your own *ancestral* background.

3. Circle the word that tells what type of workers performed deftly. Write a sentence about something you do *deftly*.

4. Underline the words that tell why the workers felt exasperation. When might you feel *exasperation*?

5. Explain why rock fragments were a problem for the workers.

6. Underline the words that tell what was somber. Write a sentence about another *somber* situation.

7. Underline the words that tell why the Chinese workers were perplexed. When might you be *perplexed*? Explain.

8. Circle the words that tell what was vividly recalled. Then, write what *vividly* means.

4

Wayson Choy
Listening and Viewing

Segment 1: Meet Wayson Choy
- How did Wayson Choy's experience growing up in Chinatown influence his writing?
- In what way are Choy's stories a bridge between two worlds?

_____

_____

_____

Segment 2: The Short Story
- What do windchimes symbolize in "The Jade Peony"?
- Why would a writer build a short story around a symbol?

_____

_____

_____

Segment 3: The Writing Process
- According to Wayson Choy, how is the process of a caterpillar turning into a butterfly similar to the writing process?
- How is your writing process similar to the process Choy describes?

_____

_____

_____

Segment 4: The Rewards of Writing
- According Wayson Choy, literature is important to all people.
- Why does he think that?
- What have you learned from or identified with in a particular piece of literature?

_____

_____

_____

_____

Name _____ Date _____

Unit 2
Learning About Short Stories

A **short story** is a work of fiction meant to be read in one sitting. It is crafted in a concise manner so that it accomplishes its purpose in relatively few words—usually 500 to 10,000.

The **plot** is the series of related events that take place in the story. During the course of the plot, events unfold. They build to a **climax** (the point of greatest tension, or the turning point) and then, during the **resolution,** come to a conclusion.

At the core of the plot is a **conflict,** or struggle. An **external conflict** occurs between characters, between an individual and a group, or between a character and a force of nature. An **internal conflict** takes place within the mind of a character.

The **characters,** the personalities who participate in the action, are usually human beings, but they may be animals or even objects. Characters are described by means of **characterization:** descriptions of characters' appearance and actions, dialogue in which characters interact with other characters and reveal information about themselves and others, and descriptions of characters' thoughts and feelings.

The **setting** is the time and place of the action. It may be the past, the present, or the future. It may be unspecific, or it may name a particular season, year, or even hour of the day. It may refer to a social, an economic, or a cultural environment, and it may specify a geographic location—a country, town, or neighborhood. The setting sets the stage for the action. It may also create a mood or an atmosphere or present a character with a conflict.

The **theme** is a story's central message or insight into life. A **stated theme** is expressed directly by the author. An implied theme is suggested by the experiences of the characters or the events and the setting of the work.

DIRECTIONS: *Write the letter of the short-story element that best describes each numbered item.*

____ 1. A freestyle swimmer finishes in first-place at an important meet.
     A. setting   B. character   C. climax

____ 2. A woman struggles against discrimination at her job.
     A. setting   B. conflict   C. resolution

____ 3. Two rivals grow to admire each other.
     A. plot   B. climax   C. resolution

____ 4. A neighborhood in San Francisco's Chinatown is described.
     A. setting   B. character   C. theme

____ 5. An obscure individual longs to become powerful and respected.
     A. internal conflict   B. external conflict   C. resolution

____ 6. A young person learns that self-confidence is a powerful quality.
     A. character   B. setting   C. theme

____ 7. A research station in Antarctica is described.
     A. theme   B. plot   C. setting

____ 8. An elderly woman recalls a long-lost love.
     A. characterization   B. theme   C. resolution

____ 9. A grandfather teaches his grandson about the respect owed to all creatures.
     A. climax   B. theme   C. characterization

"The Jade Peony" by Wayson Choy

Model Selection: Short Story

The **plot** of a short story is the series of related events that take place in the course of the story. At the core of a story's plot is usually a **conflict,** or struggle. The conflict may be **external,** in which case it features a clash between the main character and another character, between the main character and a group or society as a whole, or between the main character and a force of nature. If the conflict is **internal,** the struggle takes place within the character's mind.

The conflicts in a story typically build to a **climax,** or turning point. The events following the climax make up the outcome of the story, or the **resolution.**

Writers of short stories use methods of **characterization** to show what the characters are like. For example, writers may describe the characters' appearance and actions, quote their words, show them interacting with other characters, and describe their thoughts and feelings.

Another essential element of a short story is its setting. The **setting** is the time and place of the action. It may be general or specific, and it may include the social, economic, or cultural environment. Sometimes, the setting contributes to the **atmosphere,** or overall emotional mood, of a story. Sometimes, the setting creates a conflict.

A story's **theme** is its central message or insight about life. A **stated theme** is directly expressed by the writer. An **implied theme** is suggested by the characters' experiences, the setting, the author's tone or attitude, and/or the style of the work as a whole.

DIRECTIONS: *On the lines provided, answer these questions about "The Jade Peony."*

1. What conflicts, or problems, does Grandmama face?

   _____

   _____

2. What conflicts, or problems, does Sek-Lung (the narrator) face?

   _____

   _____

3. What conflicts, or problems, do the other members of the family face?

   _____

   _____

4. What is the setting of the story? _____

   _____

5. What role does the cultural environment play? _____

   _____

6. What is the climax of the story? Explain your answer. _____

   _____

7. In your opinion, what is the story's message about life and behavior?

   _____

"The Jade Peony" by Wayson Choy
Selection Test A

Learning About Short Stories *Identify the letter of the choice that best answers the question.*

___ 1. To which category of literature do short stories belong?
  A. nonfiction
  B. drama
  C. epic
  D. fiction

___ 2. Which of the following most accurately identifies the usual length of a short story?
  A. 100 to 200 words
  B. 200 to 1,000 words
  C. 500 to 10,000 words
  D. 50,000 to 100,000 words

___ 3. On which of the following does the plot of a short story usually focus?
  A. the point of view
  B. the conflict
  C. the characters
  D. the setting

___ 4. Which of the following correctly identifies a struggle between a character and a force of nature in a work of literature?
  A. plot
  B. suspense
  C. external conflict
  D. implied theme

Critical Reading

___ 5. Which of the following is the setting of "The Jade Peony"?
  A. Honan, China
  B. Vancouver, Canada
  C. San Francisco's Chinatown
  D. New York City's Chinatown

____ 6. Who is the central character in "The Jade Peony"?

A. the father

B. the narrator's sister

C. the juggler

D. Grandmama

____ 7. According to the narrator of "The Jade Peony," what quality in Grandmama's personality did her hands vividly convey?

A. love

B. endurance

C. talent

D. humor

____ 8. In "The Jade Peony," why do Grandmama's expeditions to find material for her windchimes cause tension in the family?

A. The family is afraid that Grandmama is wasting money.

B. The family is concerned about what the neighbors will think.

C. The family believes that Grandmama is risking her health.

D. The family believes that the expeditions make Grandmama nervous.

____ 9. In "The Jade Peony," with what does Grandmama associate her Good Fortune pendant?

A. the white cat

B. a perfect square of pink silk

C. her son's job at the newspaper

D. her memories of a long-lost love

____ 10. According to "The Jade Peony," what will Grandmama's last windchime do after her death?

A. signal the start of her funeral

B. call her ghost to hear it and return

C. send a sign to the juggler

D. comfort the family in their grief

____ 11. How does Grandmama interpret the sudden appearance of the white cat toward the end of "The Jade Peony"?

A. She sees it as an evil omen.

B. She realizes that it must be very hungry.

C. She believes that it has stolen material she needs for her windchimes.

D. She sees it as a sign that the juggler has returned to her and that she will soon die.

____ **12.** In "The Jade Peony," what does the appearance of the white cat represent?
   A. the setting
   B. characterization
   C. the climax
   D. a stated theme

____ **13.** In "The Jade Peony," what causes Grandmama's death?
   A. a heart attack
   B. a bad fall
   C. complications of pneumonia
   D. a broken heart

____ **14.** Which of the following most reasonably identifies the theme, or central message, of "The Jade Peony"?
   A. Despite the love that family members have for one another, conflicts may occur.
   B. Growing up in a large family can be frustrating, especially for adolescents.
   C. Love creates powerful bonds that can outweigh loss, suffering, and even death.
   D. We must never lose sight of the beauty and grace in the world and in our lives.

____ **15.** The tone of a short story is the writer's attitude toward the characters, the subject matter, or the audience. Which of the following best describes the writer's tone in "The Jade Peony"?
   A. anguished
   B. skeptical
   C. affectionate
   D. humorous

Essay

16. Three important elements in a short story's plot are conflict, climax, and resolution. In an essay, identify and discuss those elements in the plot of "The Jade Peony." What is the major conflict in the story? When does the climax occur? Is the conflict resolved at the end of the story? If so, how?

17. The point of view in a short story is the perspective or vantage point from which the story is told. "The Jade Peony" is told from the vantage point of Sek-Lung, Grandmama's youngest grandchild. Sek-Lung is a character in the story, and he therefore uses the pronouns *I, me,* and *our* when talking about himself and his family. In an essay, discuss the advantages and disadvantages of the first-person narration of "The Jade Peony." How does this point of view contribute to the reader's understanding of the events? How does it affect the reader's responses to Grandmama? Cite at least two details from the story in support of your main ideas.

"**The Jade Peony**" by Wayson Choy
Selection Test B

Learning About Short Stories *Identify the letter of the choice that best completes the statement or answers the question.*

____ 1. The series of related events in a short story is known as the
A. characters.
B. setting.
C. plot.
D. theme.

____ 2. Which of the following is *not* a method of characterization in a short story?
A. descriptions of a character's appearance
B. a character's words and actions
C. a character's thoughts and feelings
D. the time and place of the action

____ 3. Which of the following best defines the climax of a short story?
A. the implied theme, or message, of the story
B. the point of greatest intensity in the story's plot
C. the conclusion a reader can draw from the story's title
D. the internal conflict confronted by the story's main character

____ 4. Which of the following best defines the theme of a short story?
A. the time and place of the story's action
B. the series of related events in the story
C. the perspective from which the story is told
D. the story's central message or insight into life

____ 5. Which of the following does *not* describe an external conflict?
A. a struggle between two characters
B. a struggle in the mind of one character
C. a clash between an individual and a group
D. a struggle between a character and a force of nature

Critical Reading

____ 6. Who is the narrator of "The Jade Peony"?
A. Kiam, the oldest brother
B. the stepmother
C. the father
D. the youngest child, Sek-Lung

____ 7. Who is the main character of "The Jade Peony"?
A. the father
B. Sek-Lung
C. Grandmama
D. the juggler

____ 8. In "The Jade Peony," Grandmama initially refuses to go to the hospital when she becomes sick. Which element of a short story does that event help establish?
A. setting
B. theme
C. conflict
D. point of view

____ 9. Which word best describes the relationship between Grandmama and the narrator of "The Jade Peony"?
A. puzzling
B. strained
C. loving
D. distrustful

____ 10. Which of the following best describes the mood created by the descriptions of Grandmama's excursions in search of material for her windchimes in "The Jade Peony"?
A. ominous and a little threatening
B. adventuresome and a little mysterious
C. relaxed and very easygoing
D. solemn and somewhat respectful

____ 11. In "The Jade Peony," what color does Grandmama associate with her own spirit?
A. blue
B. white
C. pink
D. red

____ 12. According to Grandmama in "The Jade Peony," who gave her the jade carving of the peony?
A. her son
B. the juggler
C. her father
D. her grandchildren

____ 13. Why does Grandmama's search for material for her windchimes cause conflict?
A. The family is afraid that Grandmama will become ill from the cold weather.
B. The family believes that Grandmama is wasting money on the windchimes.
C. The family is ashamed because Grandmama is acting like a beggar.
D. The family is concerned that Grandmama is putting them in danger.

____ 14. According to "The Jade Peony," who accompanies Grandmama on her expeditions?
A. Jung
B. Kiam
C. Sek-Lung
D. Liang

___ 15. According to "The Jade Peony," what does Grandmama think may have happened to the juggler?
  A. He left the circus and became a farmer.
  B. He died of starvation during a famine.
  C. He emigrated from China to Canada.
  D. He fell in love with another woman.

___ 16. In "The Jade Peony," why is the last windchime she makes so important to Grandmama?
  A. After she dies, it will draw her ghost back so that she can say goodbye to the world.
  B. It will at last prove to her family that she possesses an extraordinary talent!
  C. When she is ill and about to die, its sounds will comfort her as no medicine can.
  D. After she dies, it will comfort her son and grandchildren and remind them of her.

___ 17. In "The Jade Peony," why does Grandmama claim that the white cat "was not a cat"?
  A. Grandmama's eyesight has been failing.
  B. Grandmama believes the cat is a nuisance.
  C. Grandmama has never before seen a white cat with pink eyes.
  D. Grandmama believes the cat is the spirit of her long-lost love.

___ 18. The climax of "The Jade Peony" occurs when
  A. a fire destroys the Chinese Presbyterian Church.
  B. Sek-Lung realizes that Grandmama will die soon.
  C. Grandmama runs outside to chase away a white cat.
  D. Grandmama becomes ill and is taken to the hospital.

___ 19. With which of the following is the implied theme of "The Jade Peony" most reasonably associated?
  A. the bitterness of loss
  B. the emotional turmoil of adolescence
  C. the problems of belonging to a large family
  D. the endurance of love and the acceptance of mortality

Essay

20. In a short story, characterization is the method by which a writer shows readers what the characters are like. In an essay, analyze the methods Wayson Choy uses to characterize Grandmama in "The Jade Peony." In your essay, provide examples of at least two of these methods of characterization: (1) a description of Grandmama's physical appearance, (2) descriptions of her actions, and (3) a description of Grandmama's interaction with other characters. Conclude your essay with an evaluation of Grandmama's character. In drawing your conclusion, consider how you felt about Grandmama.

21. Conflict may be called the mainspring of a short story's plot. Conflict drives the plot and engages the reader's interest, inviting the reader to become emotionally involved with the fortunes of the characters. In an essay, identify and discuss the main conflicts—both internal and external—in "The Jade Peony." How do the conflicts come together and lead to the climax of the story? Are the conflicts resolved at the end of the story? If so, how? If not, why not? Support your points with references to the story.

Starting Date _____   Ending Date _____

Unit 2: Short Stories
Part 1 Concept Map

Reading Skills and Strategies:
Make Inferences

You can make inferences about a text

by → **asking questions** → and by → **using prior knowledge**

(demonstrated in this selection)

Selection name: _____

(demonstrated in this selection)

Selection name: _____

Academic Vocabulary
words you can use to discuss making inferences

_____
_____
_____
_____

(demonstrated in this selection)

Selection name: _____

Reading Informational Materials:
Safety Signs

You can make inferences about signs

by → **evaluating visual aids for clarity and effectiveness**

Literary Analysis:
Short Story

A Short Story — has → **a conflict** — and some have → **irony**

Basic Elements of Short Stories
• Characters
• Setting
• Plot
• Theme

Literary Devices
• Foreshadowing
• Flashback
• Irony
• Dialect

Comparing Literary Works:
Setting

Setting — consists of → **place** / **time**

(demonstrated in these selections)

Selection names:
1. _____
2. _____

Part 1 Student Log

Complete this chart to track your assignments.

Writing	Extend Your Learning	Writing Workshop	Other Assignments

Unit 2: Short Stories
Part 1 Diagnostic Test 3

Read the selection. Then, answer the questions that follow.

You cannot see vitamins. They have no taste. Your body needs vitamins to stay healthy, but it cannot produce these chemicals. Therefore, you need to get these nutrients by consuming them as part of your regular diet.

Long ago, people understood the value of eating certain foods. For example, if someone in ancient Egypt experienced night blindness, a doctor would have the patient eat liver. Scientists now know that this cure was effective because liver is rich in Vitamin A. Night blindness is one symptom of a lack of Vitamin A.

Scientists identified vitamins by studying conditions like night blindness. For example, sailors on long sea voyages often became ill with a disease called scurvy. James Lind discovered that eating citrus fruits could prevent scurvy. Because sailors' diets included no fruits, their bodies lacked Vitamin C. Soon, ships began to carry citrus fruits such as limes, and sailors were given a new nickname: *limeys*. Vitamin C prevented scurvy at sea.

The United States Department of Agriculture provides recommendations for healthy nutrition. One of the department's most important objectives is providing Recommended Daily Allowances (RDAs) for vitamins. These statistics help you plan your diet to make sure you are getting all of the vitamins you need.

1. Which of the following statements about night blindness is true?
   A. Night blindness is a condition that was unknown until the twentieth century.
   B. Night blindness can be cured by eating foods that are rich in vitamin A.
   C. Night blindness is caused by eating too much liver, which is rich in vitamin A.
   D. Night blindness is caused by a lack of vitamin C, which can be found in citrus fruits.

2. What can you conclude from James Lind's work with scurvy?
   A. Long sea voyages are the cause of scurvy.
   B. The RDA for vitamin C can cause scurvy.
   C. A lack of vitamin C causes scurvy.
   D. Sailors are especially prone to scurvy and other diseases.

3. Which of the following statements about vitamins does this passage suggest?
   A. Vitamins occur naturally in different types of foods.
   B. The best way to obtain vitamins is by taking vitamin pills.
   C. Not all vitamins are necessary for a person to be healthy.
   D. An excess of certain vitamins can cause serious illnesses.

4. How did scientists like James Lind discover a particular vitamin?
   A. by creating vitamin C from chemicals in a laboratory
   B. by studying a disease caused by the lack of a certain vitamin
   C. by studying ancient Egyptian texts about diseases
   D. by analyzing how common medicines interact with certain foods

5. Why does the writer mention night blindness and scurvy?
   A. They are examples of diseases caused by lack of vitamins.
   B. They are examples of diseases that no longer exist.
   C. They are examples of diseases with an unknown cause.
   D. They are examples of conditions that are incurable.

6. Why are English sailors sometimes called *limeys*?
   A. English sailors wear lime-colored caps as part of their uniform.
   B. British trading ships carry limes as cargo from tropical countries to sell in Europe.
   C. *Limey* is a shortened form of the British exclamation *Blimey*.
   D. Sailors eat limes and other citrus fruits to prevent scurvy.

7. What do the Department of Agriculture's RDAs for vitamins specify?
   A. They specify which vitamins are most essential for good health.
   B. They specify which foods contain vitamin C and vitamin A.
   C. They specify the recommended daily allowance for each vitamin.
   D. They specify the recommended daily allowance of certain foods that are rich in vitamins.

Read the selection. Then, answer the questions that follow.

As a teenager, James Cook (1728–1779) was determined to go to sea. Initially, he apprenticed on coal ships, but he soon joined the British Royal Navy. During his lifetime, Captain Cook touched all seven continents and crossed the Pacific three times.

In 1768, the Royal Society hired Cook to lead an expedition to locate Terra Australis. This unknown continent appeared on many maps, but its existence was derived only from stories and legends. Cook's ship reached New Zealand and Australia and sailed on to New Guinea. During this three-year voyage, Cook circumnavigated the globe. His crew avoided scurvy because Cook provided them with citrus fruits, but many men died from malaria.

In 1772, the Royal Society commissioned Cook to make another voyage in search of Terra Australis. Cook and his crew were the first Europeans to cross the Antarctic Circle, and during this voyage, Cook proved that Terra Australis does not exist.

Cook's third sea voyage began in 1776. He returned to Tahiti, and he then sailed eastward to Hawaii and north to Alaska. He had imagined a scenario in which he sailed through the Bering Strait, but this proved impossible. Frustrated, Cook sailed back to Hawaii, where he was killed during a fight with natives.

8. Which of the following statements is true about James Cook before he joined the Royal Navy?
   A. He had never been to sea.
   B. He had explored Antarctica.
   C. He had discovered Australia.
   D. He had worked on coal ships.

9. What did Cook prove about Terra Australis during his second voyage for the Royal Society?
   - A. It is located very near the South Pole.
   - B. It is really the same continent as Australia.
   - C. It is an imagined continent.
   - D. It is roughly the size of Europe.

10. If you know that the Latin root -circum- means "around," what did Cook do when he "circumnavigated the globe"?
   - A. He sailed from one end of the Pacific to the other.
   - B. He sailed around Africa to the Pacific Ocean.
   - C. He sailed all around the Atlantic Ocean.
   - D. He sailed around the world.

11. Why did the sailors on Cook's ship not suffer from scurvy during their long sea voyage?
   - A. They were too sick from malaria.
   - B. They ate citrus fruits.
   - C. Scurvy was not yet a common disease.
   - D. They had all been vaccinated.

12. What was one of the purposes of The Royal Society?
   - A. to encourage exploration and discovery
   - B. to encourage literature and the arts
   - C. to encourage international trade
   - D. to encourage peace among nations

13. What happened in Alaska when Cook tried to sail through the Bering Strait?
   - A. He succeeded.
   - B. He failed.
   - C. He ran away.
   - D. He was killed.

14. Which of the following statements about James Cook is true?
   - A. He became Sir James Cook on his return to England after his third voyage.
   - B. He was hired by the Royal Society to lead four voyages of exploration.
   - C. He was the first European to set foot on Terra Australis.
   - D. He and his crew were the first Europeans to cross the Antarctic Circle.

15. Where and how did Captain James Cook die?
   - A. at sea from malaria
   - B. at sea from scurvy
   - C. in England from a heart attack
   - D. in Hawaii during a fight with natives

Study these words from "American History." Then, complete the activities.

Word List A

apparent [uh PAR ent] *adj.* easily seen or understood
It was <u>apparent</u> from her flowing tears that she was upset.

humiliation [hyoo mil ee AY shun] *n.* state of feeling ashamed or embarrassed
It was a <u>humiliation</u> to have such an awful team beat us.

impulse [IM puhls] *n.* sudden desire to do something without thinking about the results
My <u>impulse</u> was to start cheering the moment I heard the news.

intention [in TEN shuhn] *n.* plan; purpose
Our <u>intention</u> is to improve test scores by getting more tutors.

linger [LING ger] *v.* to stay on a bit longer because you want to
We wanted to <u>linger</u> and enjoy the sunset, but we had to go.

maneuvering [muh NOO ver ing] *n.* carefully planned action
It took a lot of <u>maneuvering</u> to get off work on Saturday night.

paradise [PAR uh dys] *n.* place or situation that is beautiful or very enjoyable
My mother's idea of <u>paradise</u> is a cozy chair and a good book.

suburbs [SUB urbs] *n.* areas developed near cities
Many people who work in cities prefer to live out in the <u>suburbs</u>.

Word List B

anticipated [an TIS i pay tid] *v.* looked forward to; expected
After working hard on the report, I <u>anticipated</u> a good grade.

distraught [di STRAWT] *adj.* extremely upset
We were <u>distraught</u> to hear that our favorite teacher was leaving.

embrace [em BRAYS] *v.* to give a hug
I was so happy today that I wanted to <u>embrace</u> everyone I met!

muscular [MUS kyuh luhr] *adj.* having well-developed muscles; very strong
It takes a <u>muscular</u> person to work for a moving company.

rejection [ri JEK shun] *n.* refusal to accept, allow, or approve
When his parents went out for the evening, the two-year-old cried from a sense of <u>rejection</u>.

smudged [SMUHJD] *adj.* messy or unclear
After my grandmother kisses me, she always fixes her <u>smudged</u> lipstick.

temptation [temp TAY shuhn] *n.* desire to do something wrong or foolish
It was a <u>temptation</u> to ignore the alarm and go back to sleep.

version [VER zhun] *n.* account or description from a particular point of view
If I had directed that movie, my <u>version</u> would have had a happier ending.

Name _____ Date _____

"American History" by Judith Ortiz Cofer
Vocabulary Warm-up Exercises

Exercise A *Fill in the blanks using each word from Word List A only once.*

Most people do not view the place where they live as [1] _____. Whether you hail from a farm town, a city, or the [2] _____, it is common to want to live somewhere else. Perhaps it is a natural [3] _____ to believe that greater happiness is just around the corner. Sometimes, the reason for moving on is clearly [4] _____, such as experiencing prejudice or deep [5] _____. Sometimes, the [6] _____ is to find a job. It may take [7] _____ to move from one place to the next, but few will [8] _____ if they think they are going to greener pastures. That has been the story of people through the ages!

Exercise B *Circle* T *if the statement is true or* F *if the statement is false. Then, explain your answer.*

1. A friend who is <u>distraught</u> needs comfort from you.
   T / F _____

2. A friend who is a <u>version</u> of you is your total opposite.
   T / F _____

3. Handling <u>rejection</u> is easy.
   T / F _____

4. You would never think about an event that you <u>anticipated</u>.
   T / F _____

5. If you <u>embrace</u> a friend, chances are you know each other well.
   T / F _____

6. A <u>muscular</u> appearance is a sure sign of illness.
   T / F _____

7. <u>Smudged</u> ink on your paper would be easy to read.
   T / F _____

8. A <u>temptation</u> is usually something to avoid.
   T / F _____

19

"American History" by Judith Ortiz Cofer
Reading Warm-up A

Read the following passage. Pay special attention to the underlined words. Then, read it again, and complete the activities. Use a separate sheet of paper for your written answers.

If America ever gains a fifty-first state, it could be Puerto Rico. Puerto Ricans are United States citizens. They move easily between the island and the American cities and nearby <u>suburbs</u> where many live. This relationship has made Puerto Rico a "commuter nation."

In 1898, after the Spanish-American War, the island became a colony of the United States. In 1951, Puerto Ricans voted to become a commonwealth—a self-governing U.S. territory. The first <u>impulse</u> of some Puerto Ricans was to call immediately for full independence. Their <u>intention</u> was to rid Puerto Rico of its ties to the United States. That plan was <u>apparent</u> and clearly understood when a group of nationalists tried to shoot President Harry Truman and several members of Congress.

Following that <u>maneuvering</u>, many Puerto Ricans gave up on independence in favor of statehood. No doubt this was fueled by the migration of nearly a million Puerto Ricans to America in the 1950s and 1960s. Many found life in the United States difficult. They unfairly experienced the shame and <u>humiliation</u> of being treated as second-class citizens.

In the 1970s and 1980s, many Puerto Ricans went back to the island. Perhaps they concluded that America was not a <u>paradise</u> of wealth and happiness. Or, they simply missed the country and its people.

Over time, though, this moving back and forth has become typical for many Puerto Ricans. They come to the United States to work and for education. Some commute frequently. Others <u>linger</u> in one place or the other, only reluctantly leaving when circumstances demand.

It may be this split allegiance that keeps Puerto Ricans from choosing statehood or independence whenever they vote on the issue. Puerto Ricans are U.S. citizens, but they cannot vote for president. If and when Puerto Rico decides to become a state, Hawaii will lose its status as the only island state in the United States.

1. Circle words that give clues to the meaning of <u>suburbs</u>. Do you live in the *suburbs*? Explain.

2. Underline the phrase that tells what some people's <u>impulse</u> was. Then, explain the meaning of *impulse*.

3. Circle the word that is a clue to <u>intention</u>. Write a sentence about an *intention* you have today.

4. Underline words that are clues for <u>apparent</u>. How did the nationalists make their goal *apparent*?

5. Underline words that tell the <u>maneuvering</u> of the nationalists. Write a sentence about some *maneuvering* that you did.

6. Circle the synonym for <u>humiliation</u>. Then, write a sentence using *humiliation*.

7. Circle the words that could be qualities of a <u>paradise</u>. Describe your idea of *paradise*.

8. Underline a phrase that helps you understand <u>linger</u>. Explain why you would *linger* at a friend's house.

"American History" by Judith Ortiz Cofer
Reading Warm-up B

Read the following passage. Pay special attention to the underlined words. Then, read it again, and complete the activities. Use a separate sheet of paper for your written answers.

Juan Cheo was a strong, <u>muscular</u> boy of fifteen. In the sugar cane fields of Puerto Rico, where he worked with his father after school, he could easily lift large bundles of sweet stalks into the family's rusted but reliable truck.

Occasionally, he gave in to the <u>temptation</u> of chewing on pieces of the stem to get its delicious sugary liquid. Sometimes his face, <u>smudged</u> by cinders, revealed that discarded parts of the cane had been burned. Even then, with cheeks and nose marred with soot, he would smile brilliantly. Knowing his help made a difference to the family gave Juan Cheo a sense of pride.

His father <u>anticipated</u> a healthy profit from the good harvest this year. Yet, what he thought he would get and what he received were quite different. Larger farms owned by huge companies were producing more and more sugar, and prices were plunging.

Unable to compete, Juan Cheo's father asked the bank for a loan to expand his farm. He was refused. He recognized all too clearly now that the farm would be sold.

Juan Cheo's mother was <u>distraught</u>, too deeply upset to cry, and she had a strong, sad sense of <u>rejection</u>. Yet, his father was remarkably calm. Quietly, he left the room to telephone his brother Tio Pablo, who lived in the United States. After the call, Juan Cheo's father moved toward his wife to <u>embrace</u> her lovingly. With his arms around her, he promised that all would be fine. Without asking, Juan Cheo knew: They were moving to America.

Juan Cheo's father would work with Tio Pablo in a factory and they would live with him for a while. Juan Cheo was sad at first about leaving, but he was a <u>version</u> of his father—strong in body and spirit, and possessing the same practical ability to accept what life brings. So, like his father, Juan Cheo said good-bye to the cane fields and his beautiful island, and set his sights on America.

1. Circle the clue for <u>muscular</u>. Describe what might have made Juan *muscular*.

2. Underline the <u>temptation</u> that Juan Cheo gave in to. Would you have had the same *temptation*? Explain.

3. Describe how Juan Cheo looked with a <u>smudged</u> face. Include the meaning of *smudged* in your answer.

4. Circle the phrase that is a clue to the meaning of <u>anticipated</u>. Describe something you have *anticipated* recently.

5. Underline the words that mean <u>distraught</u>. Give an antonym for *distraught*, and explain why the word has an opposite meaning.

6. Explain why Juan's mother would feel <u>rejection</u>. Include the meaning of *rejection* in your sentence.

7. Underline the description of what it means to <u>embrace</u>. Are we usually happy or sad when we *embrace* someone? Explain.

8. Describe qualities that made Juan Cheo a <u>version</u> of his father. Are you a *version* of someone in your family? Explain.

Name _____ Date _____

"American History" by Judith Ortiz Cofer
Literary Analysis: Conflict

Conflict is a struggle between opposing forces. There are two types of conflict: internal and external.

- In **internal conflict,** a character struggles with his or her own opposing feelings, beliefs, needs, or desires.
- In **external conflict,** a character struggles against an outside force, such as another character, society, or nature.

Conflict and the search for a solution are the mainspring of a story's plot. The solution, which usually occurs near the end of a story, is called the **resolution.** In some stories, the conflict is not truly resolved. Instead, the main character experiences an **epiphany,** or sudden flash of insight. Although the conflict is not resolved, the character's thoughts about it change.

A. DIRECTIONS: *"American History" contains a number of conflicts. On the following lines, briefly describe the story situation surrounding each conflict.*

1. Elena vs. Gail _____

   _____

2. Elena and Eugene vs. their classmates _____

   _____

3. Elena vs. her mother _____

   _____

4. Elena within herself _____

   _____

5. Elena vs. Eugene's mother _____

   _____

B. DIRECTIONS: *On the following lines, briefly discuss the story's ending. Does the ending contain a resolution that solves the story's main conflict, or does it contain an epiphany, a sudden flash of insight? Explain your answer by citing details from the story.*

_____

_____

_____

_____

_____

_____

Name _____ Date _____

Reading: Use Details to Make Inferences

An **inference** is a logical guess that you make based on details in a story. When you make inferences, you read between the lines to understand information that is not stated directly. To make inferences, ask yourself questions about the feelings and behavior of the characters. Here are some helpful questions to ask:

- What does this detail show about a character's motivation, or the reasons for his or her behavior?
- What does this passage say about the character's unspoken feelings and thoughts?

Detail from the story: But the day President Kennedy was shot there was a profound silence in El Building.

Inference: The residents of El Building are deeply shocked by the assassination of President Kennedy.

DIRECTIONS: *Use the following chart to make inferences about the characters' motivations and feelings from the details listed. The first item has been done for you.*

Details in the Story	My Inferences About Motivations/ Feelings
1. There was only one source of beauty and light for me that school year.	Elena likes Eugene very much.
2. Eugene was in honors classes for all his subjects; classes that were not open to me because English was not my first language, though I was a straight A student.	_____ _____ _____ _____
3. Since I had turned fourteen . . . my mother had been more vigilant than ever.	_____ _____ _____
4. "You are going out today?" The way she said 'today' sounded as if a storm warning had been issued.	_____ _____ _____ _____
5. "You live there?" She pointed up to El Building, which looked particularly ugly, like a gray prison with its many dirty windows and rusty fire escapes.	_____ _____ _____ _____

"American History" by Judith Ortiz Cofer
Vocabulary Builder

Word List

| tenement | profound | discreet | vigilant | dilapidated |

A. DIRECTIONS: *For each of the following items, think about the meaning of the italicized word, and then answer the question.*

1. How does a typical *tenement* look—elegant or run-down? _____
   _____

2. If your aunt expresses *profound* misgivings about moving to Puerto Rico, how does she feel about the move? _____
   _____

3. If your friend has been *discreet* about secrets you have told her, how do you feel about her behavior? _____
   _____

4. If a watchdog is *vigilant,* is the dog doing its job well or badly? Explain. _____
   _____

5. If you want to move into a house in good condition, would you be likely to choose a *dilapidated* one? Explain why or why not. _____
   _____

B. DIRECTIONS: *For each of the following items, write a single sentence in which you use the words as grouped.*

1. *dilapidated, tenement, profound*
   _____
   _____

2. *discreet* and *vigilant*
   _____
   _____

Name _____ Date _____

"American History" by Judith Ortiz Cofer
Support for Writing an Alternative Ending

For your alternative ending to "American History," use the following lines to jot down notes under each heading.

1. New ending grows out of earlier sequence of events:

Elena's life at school → Elena's attraction to Eugene → Mother's warnings → Study date with

Eugene → Assassination of President Kennedy → _____

_____

_____

_____

2. New ending is consistent with portrayal of characters:

Elena's character traits: _____

_____

Personality of Elena's mother: _____

_____

Eugene's character traits: _____

_____

Personality of Eugene's mother: _____

_____

3. New ending provides a resolution to the conflict:

_____

_____

_____

_____

_____

_____

Now, use your notes to write an alternative ending to "American History." Write your ending on a separate piece of paper. Be sure that your new ending resolves the main conflict in the story.

Name _____ Date _____

"American History" by Judith Ortiz Cofer
Support for Extend Your Learning

Research and Technology

Use the following lines to identify a topic for your photo essay and to make notes about ideas for your photo essay.

1. **Day of national significance and reasons why the day is significant:** _____
   _____
   _____

2. **Ideas for possible photos:** _____
   _____
   _____

3. **Possible sources for photos:** _____
   _____

4. **Possible captions for photos:** _____
   _____
   _____

Listening and Speaking

Use the following lines to make notes for your eulogy of President Kennedy.

Audience: _____

Purpose: _____

Tone: _____

President Kennedy's programs and achievements: _____
_____
_____

His appeal to young people: _____
_____
_____

His assassination: _____
_____
_____

Name _____ Date _____

"American History" by Judith Ortiz Cofer
Enrichment: History of Puerto Rico

Puerto Rico is an island in the West Indies about a 1,000 miles southeast of Miami, Florida. Puerto Rico is a Commonwealth of the United States, which means that it is a self-governing part of the United States but not a state. Its citizens are U.S. citizens. The capital of Puerto Rico is San Juan, which is located on its northern coast. Puerto Ricans, who number about $3\frac{1}{2}$ million, speak mostly Spanish, though English is also an official language.

Before the Spanish explorers arrived, Arawak Indians lived on the island. Christopher Columbus stopped there briefly in 1493, and Ponce de Leon (the Spanish explorer famous for his search for the fountain of youth) landed there in 1508. He named San Juan harbor Puerto Rico, which means "rich port" in Spanish. Beginning about 1513, African slaves worked on the island's sugar plantations. (Slavery was abolished in 1873.) In 1521, Spain established a colony in San Juan, and Puerto Rico remained a Spanish colony for more than 350 years.

During the Spanish-American War of 1898, American soldiers occupied Puerto Rico. When the war ended, the Treaty of Paris (December 10, 1898) made Puerto Rico a United States possession. The Commonwealth of Puerto Rico was established on July 25, 1952.

DIRECTIONS: *Use the background information on Puerto Rico to answer the following questions.*

1. Why is Spanish the predominant language spoken in Puerto Rico? _____

_____

_____

_____

2. How and when did Puerto Rico become part of the United States? _____

_____

_____

_____

3. When Elena and her family came to New Jersey, why were they considered U.S. citizens?

_____

_____

_____

4. Explain what a commonwealth is. _____

_____

_____

_____

"American History" by Judith Ortiz Cofer
Selection Test A

Critical Reading *Identify the letter of the choice that best answers the question.*

____ 1. At the time of Cofer's story, how old is Elena, the narrator?
   A. She is in fifth grade.
   B. She is in sixth grade.
   C. She is in ninth grade.
   D. She is in college.

____ 2. What can you infer about Gail from the incident on the playground in Cofer's story?
   A. She is mild-mannered and considerate.
   B. She is the teacher's pet.
   C. She is a bully.
   D. She studies hard.

____ 3. Early in the story, Elena describes the elderly Jewish couple who used to live next door. Which literary device is this an example of?
   A. foreshadowing
   B. flashback
   C. conflict
   D. point of view

____ 4. From the details Elena gives about her parents, which of the following is a reasonable inference?
   A. They are very wealthy.
   B. They give Elena lots of freedom.
   C. They have found it impossible to adjust to American life.
   D. They want a better life for themselves and for Elena.

____ 5. Which of the following conflicts does Elena NOT experience in "American History"?
   A. an external conflict with her mother
   B. an external conflict with Gail
   C. an internal conflict about her feelings on the day of the assassination
   D. an external conflict with Mr. DePalma

____ 6. What nicknames do the other students give to Elena and Eugene?
   A. Funny Girl and the Brain
   B. Jump Rope and Superman
   C. Skinny Bones and the Hick
   D. Dottie and Geek

_____ 7. On the day of President Kennedy's death, why is Elena so happy?

    A. She receives an A on an important test.

    B. Her family has bought a house in Clifton.

    C. Eugene has invited her to his house.

    D. Eugene tells her that he likes her.

_____ 8. What does the following passage from "American History" suggest about the people in El Building?

> For the next few days, we would observe luto in our apartment; that is, we would practice restraint and silence—no loud music or laughter. Some of the women of El Building would wear black for weeks.

    A. The people in the building had been personal friends of President Kennedy.

    B. They did not like or respect President Kennedy.

    C. They were sincerely mourning President Kennedy's death.

    D. They were registered voters and voted in every election.

_____ 9. From details about Elena's mother, what inference can you make?

    A. She worries that Elena will get poor grades and may fail.

    B. She is concerned that some of the other girls pick on Elena.

    C. She worries that Elena likes Eugene too much and may get hurt.

    D. She does not ever want to move away from El Building.

_____ 10. What happens when Elena goes to Eugene's house?

    A. Eugene's mother sharply turns her away.

    B. Eugene welcomes her warmly.

    C. Eugene's mother welcomes her warmly.

    D. Eugene's father tells Elena that Eugene is not at home.

_____ 11. Which of the following best describes the tone at the end of "American History"?

    A. mysterious

    B. joyful

    C. worried

    D. sad

_____ 12. Which of the following terms describes the flash of insight that Elena has at the end of the story?

    A. surprise ending

    B. simile

    C. epiphany

    D. internal conflict

Vocabulary and Grammar

___ 13. In which of the following sentences is the word *profound* used correctly?

    A. The people in El Building feel profound grief at the president's death.

    B. Gail shouts profound taunts and insults at Elena.

    C. The yard and trees of Eugene's house seem perfectly profound to Elena.

    D. Elena's mother feels profound about her daughter's friendship with Eugene.

___ 14. How many principal parts does a regular verb have?

    A. two

    B. three

    C. four

    D. five

___ 15. To form the past tense of a regular verb, such as *talk*, which of the following do you add?

    A. *-ed* or *-d*

    B. *-s*

    C. *-ing*

    D. the word *had*

Essay

16. In "American History," the narrator, Elena, experiences both external and internal conflicts. In an essay, summarize two of these conflicts. Tell whether the story contains a resolution for the conflicts you identify. If not, what epiphany does Elena experience at the end of the story? Support your ideas with specific references to the story.

17. In an essay, discuss the meaning of the story's title, "American History." How does the title apply to Elena's situation in the story? How does it apply to the time and place in which she finds herself? Support your ideas with specific references to the text.

"American History" by Judith Ortiz Cofer
Selection Test B

Critical Reading *Identify the letter of the choice that best completes the statement or answers the question.*

____ 1. Which of the following is the setting for "American History"?
A. Puerto Rico
B. New York City
C. Washington, D.C.
D. Paterson, New Jersey

____ 2. How do the residents of El Building differ from the people who live in the little house?
A. They are hard workers.
B. They mourn President Kennedy's death.
C. They are mostly Puerto Rican.
D. They come from Georgia.

____ 3. In Cofer's story, from the anecdote the narrator tells about jumping rope with Gail and the other girls, you can infer that
A. Gail is mild-mannered and considerate.
B. Mr. DePalma is an effective teacher.
C. Gail is something of a bully.
D. the narrator is very popular in school.

____ 4. The part of "American History" that deals with the elderly Jewish couple is an example of what literary device?
A. foreshadowing
B. flashback
C. symbolism
D. irony

____ 5. In Cofer's story, which is most likely a source of internal conflict for the narrator?
A. She likes Eugene's father because he often reads books.
B. She wants to feel bad about President Kennedy, but she feels happy about Eugene.
C. She feels bad because the elderly man who lived in the house with the yard died in June.
D. She can see inside Eugene's kitchen from her bedroom.

____ 6. Which of the following best states the main idea of this sentence from Cofer's story?
I had learned to listen to my parents' dreams, which were spoken in Spanish, as fairy tales, like the life in the island paradise of Puerto Rico before I was born.

A. The narrator does not believe that her parents tell her the truth.
B. She does not believe that her parents will achieve their dreams.
C. She wishes that her family would move back to Puerto Rico.
D. She wishes that her parents would talk in English.

____ **7.** From the details Elena gives about her parents, you can infer that they
   A. regret that they came to the United States.
   B. approve of everything Elena says and does.
   C. have found it impossible to adjust to life in the United States.
   D. aspire to a better life for themselves and Elena.

____ **8.** What do the nicknames the other students give Elena and Eugene suggest about the attitudes of these other students?
   A. They are ambitious and hard-working.
   B. They pick on people who are not like themselves.
   C. They have a great deal of school spirit.
   D. They are more interested in sports than in studies.

____ **9.** In Cofer's story, which of the following is an example of an external conflict?
   A. Elena watches the people who live in the house next door to El Building.
   B. Eugene and his family move into the house next door to El Building.
   C. Elena and Eugene become friends and walk home together from school.
   D. Elena's mother tells Elena not to become involved with Eugene.

____ **10.** On the day of President Kennedy's death, why does Elena feel elated?
   A. She learns that she has received an A on an important test.
   B. She learns that her family will move to a house in Clifton next month.
   C. Eugene has invited her to his home to study for an American history test.
   D. Eugene has told her in school that he likes her very much.

____ **11.** From the characterization of Elena's mother, you can infer that Elena's mother
   A. worries that Elena is getting bad grades in school and may fail.
   B. is concerned that some of the other girls pick on Elena and may hurt her.
   C. worries that Elena may be infatuated with Eugene and may be hurt.
   D. does not ever want to move away from El Building.

____ **12.** Which of the following is the climax of "American History"?
   A. Eugene's mother abruptly tells Elena to go home.
   B. Mr. DePalma tells his students to go home.
   C. Elena learns that President Kennedy has died.
   D. Eugene invites Elena to his home to study for a test.

____ **13.** Which of the following best describes the end of "American History"?
   A. Elena's resolves all of her external conflicts.
   B. Elena experiences an epiphany, or sudden flash of insight, about American society.
   C. Elena's parents help her to resolve both her internal and external conflicts.
   D. Elena and Eugene work successfully together to resolve their conflicts at school.

____ **14.** Which of the following best describes the tone at the end of "American History"?
   A. mysterious and puzzling
   B. joyful and optimistic
   C. sober and philosophical
   D. melancholy and disillusioned

Vocabulary and Grammar

____ 15. In which of the following sentences is the word *profound* used correctly?
A. President Kennedy's assassination plunges the nation into profound grief.
B. Gail and her friends insult Elena and call her profound names.
C. The yard and trees of Eugene's house seem profound to Elena.
D. Elena's mother feels profound about her daughter's friendship with Eugene.

____ 16. Which of the following is most nearly the opposite of *dilapidated*?
A. old-fashioned
B. decaying
C. in good repair
D. neglected

____ 17. Why can Elena's mother be described as "more *vigilant* than ever"?
A. She is sad about Kennedy's death.
B. She is watchful about her daughter.
C. She enjoys her family and friends.
D. She is gracious to Elena's friends.

____ 18. How many principal parts does a verb have?
A. two
B. three
C. four
D. five

____ 19. In which of the following sentences is the verb form correct?
A. The girls entering the double ropes in pairs.
B. The girls enters the double ropes in pairs.
C. The girls entered the double ropes in pairs.
D. The girls had entering the double ropes in pairs.

____ 20. Which of the following is the past tense of the regular verb *hope*?
A. hoped
B. hopes
C. hoping
D. had hoped

Essay

21. In "American History," the narrator is Elena, a fourteen-year-old girl who experiences several external and internal conflicts. In an essay, summarize three of her struggles between opposing forces. (The conflicts you identify may be internal or external.) Tell whether the story provides a resolution for the conflicts you identify. If there is no resolution, tell what epiphany Elena experiences at the end of the story. Be sure to include specific references to the story.

22. The setting of a story may have an important impact on the atmosphere or mood of the narrative. In an essay, analyze the ways in which the setting in "American History" is linked to the story's mood. Use specific details from the story to support your analysis.

Vocabulary Warm-up Word Lists

Study these words from "The Most Dangerous Game." Then, complete the activities.

Word List A

acknowledge [ak NAHL ij] *v.* to admit something is true or real
   After our defeat, we had to <u>acknowledge</u> that we were not a strong team.

bewilderment [bee WIL der ment] *n.* strong feeling of confusion
   Not knowing the customs of a place can create <u>bewilderment</u>.

complicated [KAHM pli kay tid] *adj.* having many parts; complex
   The report was <u>complicated</u> and required a great deal of research.

consideration [kuhn sid uh RAY shuhn] *n.* thoughtful concern for others
   Please show <u>consideration</u> and do not talk during the movie.

grisly [GRIZ lee] *adj.* horrible in an extreme way
   Movies that show a lot of blood are too <u>grisly</u> for me to watch.

particularly [pahr TIK yoo ler lee] *adv.* to a great degree
   All my relatives are fun, but I <u>particularly</u> like my oldest cousin.

superstition [soo per STI shuhn] *n.* irrational but deep-seated belief
   It may be a <u>superstition</u>, but I think my four-leaf clover brings me luck.

vivid [VIV id] *adj.* very bright; very clear
   The sky was a <u>vivid</u> blue, with not a cloud in sight.

Word List B

apprehensive [ap ree HEN siv] *adj.* worried about what may happen
   After three lost games, everyone is <u>apprehensive</u> about this one.

enthusiastically [en thoo zee AS tik lee] *adv.* with great interest
   She is so popular that everyone responds <u>enthusiastically</u> to her ideas.

inspiration [in spuh RAY shuhn] *n.* sudden bright idea
   Inventors often start with an <u>inspiration</u> that comes out of the blue.

jagged [JAG id] *adj.* sharp and uneven
   The thought of a shark's <u>jagged</u> teeth near me in the water is terrifying.

obstacle [AHB stuh kuhl] *n.* something or someone in the way
   If you give up too soon, you become an <u>obstacle</u> to your own success.

postponing [pohst POHN ing] *v.* putting off until later; delaying
   We are <u>postponing</u> our trip because will have more time next month.

precision [pri SIZH uhn] *n.* exactness or accuracy
   <u>Precision</u> is key in making clocks to ensure they tell the right time.

trait [TRAYT] *n.* quality or characteristic of a person or an animal
   The <u>trait</u> I like best in cats is their independence.

Name _____ Date _____

Vocabulary Warm-up Exercises

Exercise A *Fill in the blanks using each word from Word List A only once.*

Julie awoke and felt total [1] _____. Where was she? Nothing

was familiar, though she had to [2] _____ that the room was

[3] _____ cozy. In fact, it looked like everything in it had been chosen

with her in mind. For instance, she liked [4] _____ patterns with many

[5] _____ colors, and they were all over the room. Someone had even

shown the [6] _____ of covering her with a warm blanket. What had

happened? She recalled riding her bike, and then a black cat ran in front of her.

She did not believe that [7] _____, but, right after she saw it, she fell

hard on her head. Then, a doctor was saying that her helmet saved her from a

[8] _____ cut. What else had he said? Something about

forgetting things.

Exercise B *Circle T if the statement is true or F if the statement is false. Then, explain your answer.*

1. A friend who greets you <u>enthusiastically</u> is unhappy to see you.
   T / F _____

2. Feeling <u>apprehensive</u> about a test means you know it will be hard.
   T / F _____

3. A <u>jagged</u> road requires skillful driving.
   T / F _____

4. If you are <u>postponing</u> a trip, then you are never planning to travel.
   T / F _____

5. Having an <u>inspiration</u> means you are sleeping too much.
   T / F _____

6. A <u>trait</u> is something that only a doctor can identify.
   T / F _____

7. A person who overcomes an <u>obstacle</u> is usually admired by others.
   T / F _____

8. Both an engineer and a surgeon must show <u>precision</u> in their work.
   T / F _____

Name _____ Date _____

Read the following passage. Pay special attention to the underlined words. Then, read it again, and complete the activities. Use a separate sheet of paper for your written answers.

Those who disapprove of killing animals may view hunting as a grisly sport. However, it has provided scientists and museums with specimens for study and display.

The great nature artist and bird expert John James Audubon hunted many kinds of birds and game. His purpose was to study and draw these creatures in vivid detail. The extreme accuracy of his drawings is still considered exceptional.

Another famous hunter was Theodore Roosevelt. In 1909, after serving as president, he traveled to Africa on a safari sponsored by the Smithsonian Institution and the National Geographic Society. Although motivated by science, the expedition caused great bewilderment among his admirers. Their deep confusion is understandable. Most people acknowledge as true that Theodore Roosevelt was one of our greatest conservation presidents, who created more national parks and preserves than any other president.

What makes Roosevelt's views on hunting even more complicated is another part of his story. As a cowboy in the West in the 1880s, he saw firsthand that the buffalo was being hunted nearly to extinction. It was not superstition that caused Native Americans to believe that white men brought bad omens to their land.

As president, Theodore Roosevelt was influenced by those experiences. He worked particularly hard, to a degree not seen after him, to ensure that the lands of the West would remain beautiful for future generations to enjoy.

The origin of the "teddy bear" is another example of his consideration for living creatures. On one outdoor adventure he saved the life of a young bear cub. The story of his kindness spread, and a toy maker created a stuffed bear in his honor.

In the end, perhaps what motivated Theodore Roosevelt was the chance to be part of nature. As he once wrote, "The hunter who wanders through these lands sees sights which ever afterward remain fixed in his mind."

1. Circle the word that grisly describes. Based on the passage, why do some people view hunting as *grisly*?

2. Underline the words that help you understand the meaning of vivid detail. Give an antonym for *vivid* that would change that meaning.

3. Underline the words that are clues to bewilderment. Might a new student feel *bewilderment*? Explain.

4. Circle a word that is a clue to acknowledge. In your own words, tell why people *acknowledge* Roosevelt as a great conservation president.

5. Underline what the passage says is complicated. Give an antonym for *complicated*.

6. Circle the words that give clues to superstition. Describe a common *superstition*.

7. Underline a phrase that gives a clue to particularly. Describe something that is *particularly* hard or easy for you.

8. Circle the word that is a clue to consideration. How could students show more *consideration* at school?

"The Most Dangerous Game" by Richard Connell
Reading Warm-up B

Read the following passage. Pay special attention to the underlined words. Then, read it again, and complete the activities. Use a separate sheet of paper for your written answers.

Finn opened the door of the lighthouse to a beautiful sunrise. The early morning was cool, but soon the day would be scorching. That was always the Caribbean weather, which is why, Finn knew, tourists could not get enough of his island.

Finn loved the island, too, not so much for its climate as for providing one <u>inspiration</u> after another. With the vast ocean all around, he was forever finding objects that he could use for some purpose or that triggered amazing tales in his mind of their journeys across the sea.

Living in the lighthouse was a definite advantage— since it was the highest point on the island, no <u>obstacle</u> could block his view. From his bedroom window at sunset the day before, he had noticed something shining on the farthest shore. He had wanted to set out immediately, yet while <u>postponing</u> his expedition was difficult, waiting was wiser. Traveling the <u>jagged</u> cliffs, with their razor-sharp stones, was dangerous at night.

He told his mother of his plan, expecting her to be <u>apprehensive</u>. She always worried that something might happen to her children. In fact, if Finn were to name a <u>trait</u> that distinguished his mother, it was "constant worry." This time she surprised him, simply reminding him to be careful. His sister was eager to go along, <u>enthusiastically</u> offering to carry the metal detector Finn used on his island searches, but she got a firm "no."

Finally, Finn was ready. He pulled out his compass and, with careful <u>precision</u>, determined the exact direction to hike. In an hour he reached the beach, with the object just over the next sand dune. Finn crept up and peered over the top. Suddenly, a silvery orb loomed in his face. He screamed—then laughed as he realized it was a balloon, caught in driftwood, with a capsule attached. Inside, Finn found a letter from a girl in Tampa, Florida, asking the finder for a postcard to show where her balloon landed. Finn blushed at the thought of writing this unknown girl. Even so, this was his best find ever!

1. Underline the sentence that gives clues to the meaning of <u>inspiration</u>. Have you had an *inspiration* lately? Explain.

2. Circle the verb that is a clue to <u>obstacle</u>. What is a learning *obstacle* a student might have, and what could be done about it?

3. Circle a word that is a clue to <u>postponing</u>. Does *postponing* mean the same as canceling? Explain.

4. Underline the phrase that gives a clue to <u>jagged</u>. Give an antonym for *jagged*.

5. Underline the sentence that explains why Finn's mother was <u>apprehensive</u>. Give an antonym for *apprehensive*.

6. Give a synonym for <u>trait</u>. Name a *trait* that distinguishes you, and why.

7. Circle a word that is a clue to <u>enthusiastically</u>. Describe how someone behaves *enthusiastically*.

8. Underline words that are clues to <u>precision</u>. Name a noun that is a synonym for *precision* and an adjective that means the opposite.

Name _____ Date _____

"The Most Dangerous Game" by Richard Connell
Literary Analysis: Conflict

Conflict is a struggle between opposing forces. There are two types of conflict: internal and external.

- In **internal conflict,** a character struggles with his or her own opposing feelings, beliefs, needs, or desires.
- In **external conflict,** a character struggles against an outside force, such as another character, society, or nature.

Conflict and the search for a solution are the mainspring of a story's plot. The solution, which usually occurs near the end of a story, is called the **resolution.** In some stories, the conflict is not truly resolved. Instead, the main character experiences an **epiphany,** or sudden flash of insight. Although the conflict is not resolved, the character's thoughts about it change.

A. DIRECTIONS: *"The Most Dangerous Game" contains a number of conflicts. On the following lines, briefly describe the story situations surrounding each conflict.*

1. Rainsford vs. nature _____

_____

_____

2. General Zaroff vs. the "visitors" to his island _____

_____

_____

3. Rainsford vs. General Zaroff _____

_____

_____

4. Rainsford within himself _____

_____

_____

B. DIRECTIONS: *On the following lines, briefly discuss the story's ending. Does the ending contain a resolution that solves the story's main conflict? Have Rainsford's experiences changed his views about hunting? Explain your answer by citing details from the story.*

_____

_____

_____

_____

_____

"The Most Dangerous Game" by Richard Connell
Reading: Use Details to Make Inferences

An **inference** is a logical guess that you make based on details in a story. When you make inferences, you read between the lines to understand information that is not stated directly. To make inferences, ask yourself questions about the feelings and behavior of the characters. Here are some helpful questions to ask.

- What does this detail show about a character's motivation, or the reasons for his or her behavior?
- What does this passage say about the character's unspoken feelings and thoughts?

Example from "The Most Dangerous Game":

Detail from the story: "I can't believe you are serious, General Zaroff. This is a grisly joke."

Inference: Rainsford has just begun to realize that Zaroff hunts humans.

A. DIRECTIONS: *Use the following chart to make inferences from the details listed. The first item has been done for you.*

Details in the Story	My Inferences About Motivations/ Feelings
1. Rainsford tells Whitney that there are only two classes of people: hunters and huntees.	Rainsford begins the story with a matter-of-fact, almost hard-boiled attitude.
2. Rainsford asks Zaroff to excuse him for the night because he feels sick.	
3. Zaroff tells Rainsford how upset he was at the death of his dog Lazarus.	
4. Rainsford is able to rig up several ingenious traps, such as the Burmese tiger pit and a Malay mancatcher.	

B. DIRECTIONS: *Do you think "The Most Dangerous Game" has a serious theme, or message about human nature or behavior? Or, is it primarily a suspenseful adventure story intended to entertain readers rather than to make a point? Explain your answer with specific references to details in the story.*

_____

_____

_____

"The Most Dangerous Game" by Richard Connell
Vocabulary Builder

Word List

palpable	indolently	scruples	naive	futile

A. DIRECTIONS: *In each of the following items, think about the meaning of the italicized word, and then answer the question.*

1. What is the danger if you approach a research paper assignment *indolently*?

   _____

   _____

2. How are you feeling if you have *scruples* about doing something?

   _____

   _____

3. How would you feel if you make a long and *futile* journey?

   _____

4. In most cases, why is it easy to fool or trick a *naive* person?

   _____

5. If the tension during the final two minutes of a game is *palpable,* do you think the specta-tors feel suspense or not? Explain.

   _____

B. DIRECTIONS: *For each of the following items, write a single sentence in which you use the words as grouped.*

1. *palpable* and *scruples*

   _____

   _____

2. *indolently* and *futile*

   _____

   _____

3. *naive* and *scruples*

   _____

   _____

"The Most Dangerous Game" by Richard Connell
Support for Writing an Alternative Ending

For your alternative ending to "The Most Dangerous Game," use the following lines to jot down notes under each heading.

1. **New ending grows out of earlier sequence of events:**

Rainsford falls off yacht and lands on island →Rainsford meets General Zaroff and learns of Zaroff's "game" →Rainsford is forced to become the "huntee" →Rainsford confronts Zaroff in the general's bedroom → _____

_____

_____

_____

2. **New ending is consistent with portrayal of characters:**

Rainsford's character traits: _____

_____

Zaroff's character traits: _____

_____

3. **New ending provides a resolution to the conflict:**

_____

_____

_____

_____

_____

_____

_____

_____

Now, use your notes to write an alternative ending to "The Most Dangerous Game." Write your ending on a separate piece of paper. Be sure that your new ending resolves the main conflict in the story.

"The Most Dangerous Game" by Richard Connell
Support for Extend Your Learning

Research and Technology

Use the following lines to identify a topic for your photo essay and to conduct research on this topic.

1. **Choice of big-game species:** _____
   _____

2. **Ideas for possible photos:** _____
   _____
   _____

3. **Possible sources for photos:** _____
   _____

4. **Possible captions for photos:** _____
   _____
   _____
   _____

Listening and Speaking

Use the following spaces to make notes for a speech to be presented to an audience of big-game hunters. Remember that you are speaking as Rainsford. Be sure to take a position, stating whether or not your attitude toward big-game hunting has changed as a result of the story events in "The Most Dangerous Game."

Audience: _____

Purpose: _____

Tone: _____

What I will say: _____
_____
_____
_____
_____
_____
_____
_____
_____

"The Most Dangerous Game" by Richard Connell
Enrichment: Dealing With Competition

General Zaroff develops his gruesome variation on hunting because he says that hunting animals is no longer a challenge for him. He is driven by competition: His need for ever-greater challenges spins out of control.

Competition can be a positive quality in life as a whole, and specifically in the environment of the workplace. However, competition can also be troublesome if carried to an extreme.

Role Play Imagine that you are a friend of General Zaroff's, perhaps a fellow officer or a hunting companion. Zaroff confides his feelings to you long before he starts to hunt human beings. With a partner playing General Zaroff, role-play a conversation in which you give him advice about how he might channel his competitive spirit into other pursuits.

Apply In each of the following everyday situations, a competitive situation causes problems. What advice would you give to the people in each situation? Write your advice on the lines provided.

1. Jose and his younger brother Miguel play one-on-one basketball every night. Jose is older and taller than Miguel and always wins. Miguel insists on playing, however, and he insists on keeping score. _____
   _____
   _____

2. Competition among teams in a softball club has grown fierce. The players care only about the standings. No one seems to be enjoying the game itself anymore. _____
   _____
   _____

3. Marian has the best voice in the school chorus. During tryouts, she always wins the solos for the choral concerts. The other singers are feeling left out and are thinking of quitting the chorus. _____
   _____
   _____

4. In science class, one student dominates the discussions and interrupts other students who attempt to express ideas. No one wants to be in class with this student anymore.
   _____
   _____

5. You and a friend are working part time at the same business. You would like to work together, but your friend is continually trying to outdo you in every task. You are afraid that this will make you look bad and you will be fired. _____
   _____
   _____

"American History" by Judith Ortiz Cofer
"The Most Dangerous Game" by Richard Connell
Build Language Skills: Vocabulary

Word Roots *-spec-,-circum-*

The Latin root *-spec-* means "to look" or "to see." This root appears in English words that have to do with "looking at," "looking upon," or "seeing" something. For example, when you discuss an *aspect* of a story, you look at a particular part or feature. When you *inspect* something, you look at it carefully.

The Latin root *-circum-* means "around" or "surrounding." A *circumstance* is a fact or an event that surrounds another event. To *circumvent* a difficulty or an obstacle is to find a way around it.

A. DIRECTIONS: *Use a dictionary to look up the origin of each of the following words containing the roots -spec- and -circum-. Write one meaning for each word. Then, write a sentence in which you use the word in a context that makes its meaning clear.*

1. speculate Meaning: _____

   Sentence: _____

2. specter Meaning: _____

   Sentence: _____

3. circumlocution Meaning: _____

   Sentence: _____

4. circumscribe Meaning: _____

   Sentence: _____

Academic Vocabulary Practice

B. DIRECTIONS: *Answer each question using the underlined academic vocabulary word.*

1. Do appeals to <u>emotion</u> usually involve the head more than the heart or vice versa?

   _____

2. What is one way you can <u>categorize</u> the characters in a story or play?

   _____

3. What literary <u>element</u> do writers use to describe the circumstances of a story, such as the time and place that the events occur?

   _____

4. What elements in a story often serve as clues to a character's <u>motives</u>?

   _____

5. Why is the point of view usually an important <u>aspect</u> of a story?

   _____

"American History" by Judith Ortiz Cofer
"The Most Dangerous Game" by Richard Connell
Build Language Skills: Grammar

Regular Verbs

A verb has four principal parts: the present, the present participle, the past, and the past participle. Most verbs in English are regular. **Regular verbs** form the past and the past participle by adding *-ed* or *-d* to the present form.

The past and past participle of regular verbs have the same form. In the following chart of principal parts, *has* is in parentheses in front of the past participle to remind you that this verb form is a past participle only if it is used with a helping verb.

Notice that the final consonant is sometimes doubled to form the present participle (*tapping*) as well as the past and the past participle (*tapped*). Notice also that the final *e* may be dropped in forming the present participle (*wiping*).

Principal Parts of Regular Verbs			
Present	**Present Participle**	**Past**	**Past Participle**
play	(is) playing	played	(has) played
tap	(is) tapping	tapped	(has) tapped
wipe	(is) wiping	(is) wiped	(has) wiped

A. PRACTICE: *Write the answer(s) to each of the following questions on the lines provided.*

1. Give the four principal parts of the following verbs:

   walk: _____

   hunt: _____

   place: _____

   rip: _____

2. What do you add to form the past tense of regular verbs? _____

B. Writing Application: *Read the following sentences and notice the verb in italics. If the verb is used correctly, write* Correct *in the space provided. If the verb is not used correctly, rewrite the sentence using the correct form of the verb.*

1. In Paterson, New Jersey, Elena *lived* in El Building with her family.

   _____

2. After school started, Elena *looking* for Eugene in all her classes.

   _____

3. Mr. DePalma has *ask* us to line up in front of him.

   _____

4. Rainsford was exhausted when he *arrive* on the island.

   _____

"The Most Dangerous Game" by Richard Connell
Selection Test A

Critical Reading *Identify the letter of the choice that best answers the question.*

_____ 1. Which of the following best describes "The Most Dangerous Game"?
A. a classic stuggle between rich and poor
B. a bitter attack on hunting
C. a deadly contest between two hunters
D. a superstitious tale told by sailors

_____ 2. How does Connell create suspense at the beginning of the story?
A. The story begins with dialogue, not description.
B. Whitney refers to Captain Nielsen, a mysterious figure.
C. Whitney describes the mysterious reputation of the island they are passing.
D. Whitney and Rainsford plan to go hunting in the Amazon.

_____ 3. Which of the following events comes first in "The Most Dangerous Game"?
A. Rainsford spears Ivan.
B. Rainsford falls overboard.
C. Rainsford sleeps in Zaroff's bed.
D. Rainsford leaps into the sea.

_____ 4. Which of the following identifies the main conflict in "The Most Dangerous Game"?
A. Rainsford vs. Zaroff
B. Ivan vs. Zaroff
C. Rainsford vs. the ocean
D. Rainsford vs. Ivan

_____ 5. Which of the following best describes General Zaroff's problem before he invents his "game"?
A. He loves hunting but hates to see animals suffer.
B. He hates Ivan but needs him for company.
C. He cares only for hunting, but hunting has begun to bore him.
D. He hates Rainsford but must be kind to him.

_____ 6. Why does Zaroff not consider his sport immoral?
A. He does not directly kill his victims.
B. He gives his visitors plenty of good food and exercise.
C. He respects his victims.
D. He believes that the weak were put on earth to give the strong pleasure.

____ 7. Zaroff tells Rainsford that the visitors to the island always choose to go hunting with him. What can you infer from this remark?

A. The visitors like to play Zaroff's game.

B. They have formed secret plans to escape.

C. They are willing to take their chances in the hunt rather than be tortured by Ivan.

D. Zaroff tricks them into believing that the hunt will not hurt them.

____ 8. What can you infer from Zaroff's careful studying of Rainsford during their first dinner together?

A. Zaroff is sizing up Rainsford's appetite.

B. He is trying to find out what kind of an enemy Rainsford would make.

C. He is wondering if Rainsford suspects anything is wrong.

D. He wants to make Rainsford uncomfortable.

____ 9. Which of the following is the resolution of the main conflict in "The Most Dangerous Game"?

A. Rainsford appears in Zaroff's bedroom.

B. Zaroff finds Rainsford's circular trail.

C. Rainsford dives into the sea.

D. One of Zaroff's dogs falls into Rainsford's trap.

____ 10. Which character in "The Most Dangerous Game" experiences the most important internal conflicts?

A. Whitney

B. Zaroff

C. Ivan

D. Rainsford

____ 11. In the conflict with Rainsford, what factor contributes to Zaroff's defeat?

A. his own overconfidence

B. his careless mistakes

C. his inferior hunting skills

D. the loss of Ivan

Vocabulary and Grammar

____ 12. Which of the following words is most nearly opposite in meaning to *naive*?

A. careful

B. happy

C. sophisticated

D. worried

____ **13.** In which of the following sentences is the word *scruples* used correctly?

    A. Rainsford strikes out in the direction of the scruples, swimming steadily.

    B. Rainsford realizes that Zaroff has absolutely no moral scruples about his brand of hunting.

    C. Rainsford fears he might be trapped in the scruples of quicksand.

    D. Whitney tells Rainsford of the mysterious scruples surrounding the island.

____ **14.** What do you add to a regular verb, such as *hate* or *hunt,* to form the past tense?

    A. *-ing*

    B. *-s* or *-es*

    C. an apostrophe

    D. *-d* or *-ed*

____ **15.** In which of the following sentences is the verb used corectly?

    A. Rainsford's mind working frantically.

    B. The baying of the hounds stop abruptly.

    C. Rainsford jumped far out into the sea.

    D. Zaroff's quarry escaping him.

Essay

16. After his first meeting with Zaroff, Rainsford spends a sleepless night because he cannot "quiet his brain." In a brief essay, discuss what is probably going through Rainsford's head. Describe his reactions to his first day on Ship-Trap Island. Be sure to give reasons and examples from the story to explain why Rainsford responds this way.

17. The ending of "The Most Dangerous Game" suggests that Rainsford changes his attitude toward big-game hunting. What are his thoughts about hunting animals at the beginning of the story? How does he most likely feel about hunting animals after his experience with Zaroff? In a brief essay, discuss your ideas and answers to these questions.

"The Most Dangerous Game" by Richard Connell
Selection Test B

Critical Reading *Identify the letter of the choice that best completes the statement or answers the question.*

____ 1. "The Most Dangerous Game" is best described as a story about
   A. a conflict between the wealthy and the poverty-stricken.
   B. a bitter attack on the habits of hunters.
   C. a deadly contest between two skillful hunters.
   D. an amusing adventure told by superstitious sailors.

____ 2. How does Connell create suspense at the very beginning of the story?
   A. The story begins with dialogue instead of description.
   B. Whitney refers to Captain Nielsen, but Nielsen does not appear.
   C. Whitney tells Rainsford about the mysterious reputation of the island in the distance.
   D. Whitney and Rainsford discuss the prospects of hunting up the Amazon.

____ 3. What can you infer from Zaroff's careful studying of Rainsford during their first dinner together?
   A. Zaroff is sizing up Rainsford's appetite in order to determine his strength.
   B. He is trying to determine what kind of foe Rainsford would make.
   C. He is wondering if Rainsford suspects that anything is awry.
   D. He wants to make Rainsford uncomfortable.

____ 4. Which of the following best describes the problem Zaroff experiences before he devised his "most dangerous game"?
   A. He loved hunting but could not bear to see any animal suffer and die.
   B. He despised all human beings, but people kept coming to visit him on his island.
   C. He cared only for hunting, but hunting had begun to bore him.
   D. He hated Rainsford but had to show him hospitality.

____ 5. Why does General Zaroff not consider his sport immoral?
   A. He is not responsible for his victims' deaths.
   B. He rescues his victims from a certain death.
   C. He sympathizes with his victims and provides them with plenty of good food and exercise.
   D. He believes that the weak were put on earth to give the strong pleasure.

____ 6. Which of the following describes the main conflict of "The Most Dangerous Game"?
   A. external conflict: Rainsford vs. Zaroff
   B. external conflict: Ivan vs. Zaroff
   C. external conflict: Rainsford vs. the ocean
   D. internal conflict: Rainsford vs. himself

____ 7. When Zaroff tells Rainsford that his visitors always choose to go hunting, we can infer that
   A. they are enthusiastic about playing Zaroff's game.
   B. they have secret plans for a daring escape from the island.
   C. they are willing to take their chances in the hunt rather than be tortured by Ivan.
   D. they believe that the hunt is just a game and Zaroff will not hurt them.

____ 8. In the conflict with Rainsford, Zaroff is defeated by Rainsford's hunting skills and also by his
   A. own overconfidence.
   B. loss of Ivan.
   C. inattention to detail.
   D. inferior hunting skills.

____ 9. As he tries to escape from Zaroff, Rainsford also struggles to overcome his own feelings of
   A. anger.
   B. loneliness.
   C. honor.
   D. panic.

____ 10. You can infer that Rainsford succeeds largely because
   A. he is resourceful and refuses to play by Zaroff's rules.
   B. he considers Zaroff's "sport" to be cold-blooded murder.
   C. he has no sympathy for the animals he hunts.
   D. he believes life is for the strong, to be lived by the strong.

____ 11. Which of the following is the resolution of the story's main conflict?
   A. Rainsford appears in Zaroff's bedroom.
   B. Zaroff finds Rainsford's circular trail.
   C. Rainsford dives into the sea.
   D. One of Zaroff's dogs falls into Rainsford's trap.

____ 12. What can you infer from the following sentence about what Rainsford sees after he falls from the yacht?
   "The lights of the yacht became faint and ever-vanishing fireflies; then they were blotted out entirely by the night."
   A. There are many fireflies on the island.
   B. Rainsford has lost his glasses.
   C. The yacht is moving away from him.
   D. The yacht is moving closer to him.

____ 13. Which of the following statements by General Zaroff adds to the suspense of the story?
   A. "After the debacle in Russia I left the country, for it was imprudent for an officer of the Czar to stay there."
   B. "I was about to have my dinner when you came. I'll wait for you."
   C. "I've read your book about hunting snow leopards in Tibet, you see."
   D. "To date I have not lost."

Vocabulary and Grammar

____ 14. In which sentence is the word *indolently* used correctly?
   A. Rainsford hears several shots coming indolently from the island.
   B. General Zaroff rushes indolently to his dinner table.
   C. Rainsford reclines in a chair on deck, indolently puffing on his pipe.
   D. Indolently awake, Rainsford ponders his predicament throughout the night.

____ 15. Which word is most nearly the opposite of *futile* as it is used in the following sentence?

"He saw that straight flight was futile; inevitably it would bring him face to face with the sea."

A. unusual
B. effective
C. unimportant
D. useless

____ 16. What do you add to a regular verb, such as *escape*, to form the past tense?

A. *-ing*
B. *-s* or *-es*
C. an apostrophe
D. *-d* or *-ed*

____ 17. Which word best fits in the blank?

Rainsford eventually realizes that Zaroff has absolutely no _____ about his particular type of hunting.

A. ambition
B. prospects
C. complaints
D. scruples

____ 18. The form of a regular verb that ends in *-ing* is called the

A. present.
B. present participle.
C. past.
D. past participle.

____ 19. In which of the following sentences is the verb used correctly?

A. Rainsford struggling to the surface.
B. Rainsford remember the sound of shots.
C. They discussed hunting.
D. Rainsford smiling at Ivan.

Essay

20. At the beginning of the story, Rainsford states that there are only two classes of people in the world—the hunters and the huntees. Do you agree? Write a brief essay in which you explain your answer. How has your understanding of "The Most Dangerous Game" clarified your opinion?

21. The main conflict of "The Most Dangerous Game" pits two characters against each other in a truly perilous combat. While Sanger Rainsford would probably hesitate to admit it, he and General Zaroff actually have much in common. Write a brief essay in which you explore the ways in which Rainsford and Zaroff are alike and the ways in which they differ.

22. Suspense is the quality of a story that makes you want to keep reading until you find out what happens. Writers create suspense by communicating a sense of uncertainty and danger. In a brief essay, identify three suspenseful episodes in "The Most Dangerous Game," and analyze the ways in which the author makes you want to keep reading. Be as specific as possible in your analysis.

Vocabulary Warm-up Word Lists

Study these words from "The Gift of the Magi." Then, complete the activities.

Word List A

calculated [KAL kyoo lay tid] *v.* estimated; figured with numbers
   Based on when my train got in, I <u>calculated</u> the time when I would arrive for the party.

craved [KRAYVD] *v.* wanted to an extreme degree
   When I was on my diet, I <u>craved</u> candy and other sweets.

hysterical [his TER uh kuhl] *adj.* very excited, frightened, or angry
   There were <u>hysterical</u> reactions to the news that the president had been shot.

immediate [i MEE dee it] *adj.* happening or done at once
   An <u>immediate</u> consequence of the fight was suspension for everyone.

metaphor [MET uh fawr] *n.* way of describing something by calling it something else
   "Dark clouds" may be a <u>metaphor</u> for something bad happening.

privilege [PRIV uh lij] *n.* special right or advantage
   It is a <u>privilege</u> to live in a country where everyone may vote.

rippling [RIP ling] *v.* flowing like gentle waves
   It was a beautiful sight to see the flag <u>rippling</u> in the breeze.

sacrificed [SAK ruh fyst] *v.* gave up something of value
   The prisoner of war never <u>sacrificed</u> his honor by telling what he knew.

Word List B

adorned [uh DAWRND] *adj.* decorated
   The house was <u>adorned</u> with festive holiday decorations.

agile [A juhl] *adj.* able to move easily or quickly; flexible
   A basketball player must be <u>agile</u> to navigate around the other players.

generosity [jen uh RAH suh tee] *n.* willingness to give
   It was his <u>generosity</u> that inspired others to donate to the fund.

inconsequential [in kahn se KWEN shuhl] *adj.* not important
   I am not shopping, so it is <u>inconsequential</u> whether I go to the mall.

prosperity [pros PER uh tee] *n.* condition of having wealth or good fortune
   In some cultures, having many farm animals is evidence of <u>prosperity</u>.

scrutiny [SKROO tuh nee] *n.* close and careful examination
   Since the call for uniforms, what we wear to school is under <u>scrutiny</u>.

sequence [SEE kwens] *n.* order in which something is arranged or occurs
   In the <u>sequence</u> of events, he arrived after the murder but before the police.

sentiments [SEN tuh ments] *n.* feelings or emotions
   The candidate found that the <u>sentiments</u> of the people were against her.

Name _____ Date _____

"The Gift of the Magi" by O. Henry
Vocabulary Warm-up Exercises

Exercise A *Fill in the blanks using each word from Word List A only once.*

Have you ever experienced a fit of [1] _____ laughter? I wish I could offer a [2] _____ to describe what it is like. You might think of it as waves of laughter that start [3] _____ and build to a tidal wave of belly laughs. I have [4] _____ that a good laugh can go on and on. When others feel the [5] _____ impact of all that jolliness, in a flash, they are laughing, too— but not always! You may find you have [6] _____ a friendship if you laugh at the WRONG moment, say when a friend who has [7] _____ your attention for a serious discussion thinks you are making fun. Those who grant you the [8] _____ of hearing their secrets do not want that right abused!

Exercise B *Circle* T *if the statement is true or* F *if the statement is false. Then, explain your answer.*

1. If you have <u>adorned</u> a room, you have made it plainer.
   T / F _____

2. Only rich people can show <u>generosity</u>.
   T / F _____

3. It is foolish to worry about something that is <u>inconsequential</u>.
   T / F _____

4. An <u>agile</u> person looks more awkward than others.
   T / F _____

5. People should always inspect a used car with <u>scrutiny</u> before buying it.
   T / F _____

6. A ragged appearance is a sure sign of <u>prosperity</u>.
   T / F _____

7. If you show your <u>sentiments</u>, others know what you are thinking and feeling.
   T / F _____

8. Two events that happen in <u>sequence</u> can take place at exactly the same time.
   T / F _____

Name _____   Date _____

Read the following passage. Pay special attention to the underlined words. Then, read it again, and complete the activities. Use a separate sheet of paper for your written answers.

The rise of the department store began in the "Gilded Age" of the late 1800s. The writer Mark Twain first used the term. It was a <u>metaphor</u> that described an America that glittered with the wealth of a few. Underneath, though, it was dark with poverty and struggle. Most people <u>sacrificed</u> for the little they had, counting pennies and giving up long hours to hard work.

However, those with money offered rich possibilities for eager businessmen. They <u>calculated</u> that great profits could be made with a new kind of store. They expected that if customers had the <u>privilege</u> of finding everything they needed in one location, those delighted shoppers might be tempted to buy more. They were right. It worked to everyone's advantage!

The department store was an <u>immediate</u> success. Almost instantly an area of New York City known as the Ladies' Mile was <u>rippling</u> with waves of customers moving in and out of grand stores. There, all the goods that people <u>craved</u>, or desperately wanted, were under one roof. Many features of modern shopping, such as free samples and product demonstrations, were born in this era.

The opening of one "shopping resort" in 1896 attracted 150,000 <u>hysterical</u> shoppers. Their uncontrolled excitement matched the over-the-top quality of the place. Every type of merchandise could be found within the giant store's walls. There was also a telegraph and long-distance telephone office. There was a foreign money exchange, stock trading, and a dentist's office.

Today, the department store is more often part of a sprawling mall than a stand-alone structure. Nonetheless, the idea of drawing people to one place to meet their consumer needs is as alive and well today as in the day of the "shopping resort."

1. Circle the term that the passage calls a <u>metaphor</u>. Underline the explanation of this *metaphor* in the passage.

2. Underline two ways the narrator says most people <u>sacrificed</u> to get the little they had.

3. Underline what the businessmen <u>calculated</u>. Explain why they believed this.

4. Circle the word that is a clue to the meaning of <u>privilege</u>. Describe a *privilege* that you enjoy.

5. Circle the words that are clues to the meaning of <u>immediate</u>. Describe what a store that was an *immediate* success would be like.

6. Circle the words that tell what was <u>rippling</u> on the Ladies' Mile. Explain the meaning of *rippling*.

7. Underline the words that are clues to the meaning of <u>craved</u>. Name a word that is the opposite of *craved*.

8. Underline the words that are clues to the meaning of <u>hysterical</u>. How might *hysterical* shoppers behave?

Name _____ Date _____

"The Gift of the Magi" by O. Henry
Reading Warm-up B

Read the following passage. Pay special attention to the underlined words. Then, read it again, and complete the activities. Use a separate sheet of paper for your written answers.

Over the centuries, wigs have been popular accessories. Since earliest times, wigs have been used to enhance beauty. In ancient Egypt, both men and women of nobility wore wigs of human hair <u>adorned</u> with flowers and gold ornaments on special occasions. There are paintings of the dead wearing wigs, which is far from <u>inconsequential</u>. Instead, it is a sign that the wig was important to the Egyptians. They believed that everything needed in the afterlife must be buried with the dead.

Perhaps the expression "blonds have more fun" got its start in ancient Rome. Many Roman women expressed <u>sentiments</u> that blond hair was better than their own dark hair. The solution? Wigs were made from the hair of blond captives. Apparently, Romans were such slaves to fashion that a likeness of one noblewoman was fitted with a <u>sequence</u> of different marble wigs, one following the other as styles changed.

Throughout history, the wearing of wigs was a sign of <u>prosperity</u>. It was the wealthy who cared about and could afford the elaborate headpieces when they were in fashion. Wigs would go out of style and then be brought back by a king or queen, such as Louis XIII of France, who was bald at an early age. Unlike men's hairpieces now, the wig Louis made popular was not meant to disguise hair loss. It did not take much <u>scrutiny</u> to recognize that the king's long and curly locks were not his own.

In the 1700s, wigs for women were designed with support wires and powder that raised hair three feet in the air. Some included cages with live birds and miniature ships. It would take an <u>agile</u> woman to move easily in such a headpiece without tipping over!

These days, wigs are mainly worn by entertainers and those who have lost their hair due to illness. In that regard, the act of <u>generosity</u> in "The Gift of the Magi" is still repeated. Some people donate their hair for wigs that go to children with cancer.

1. Underline the words that give clues to the meaning of <u>adorned</u>. Then, write your own explanation of *adorned*.

2. Circle the word that means the opposite of <u>inconsequential</u>. Describe something that you view as *inconsequential*. Tell why.

3. Underline the phrase that explains the <u>sentiments</u> of Roman woman about hair. Do you use *sentiments* to describe facts or opinions? Explain.

4. Underline the phrase that explains the meaning of <u>sequence</u>. Write a *sequence* of events in your day.

5. Circle the word that gives a clue to the meaning of <u>prosperity</u>. Name an antonym for *prosperity*.

6. Give a synonym for <u>scrutiny</u>. Would you feel comfortable if you were under *scrutiny*? Explain.

7. Underline words that are clues for <u>agile</u>. Is it a compliment to be called *agile*? Explain.

8. Underline the act of <u>generosity</u> described. How can you show *generosity*?

"The Gift of the Magi" by O. Henry
Literary Analysis: Irony and Surprise Ending

Irony is a difference or a contradiction between appearance and reality or between what is expected and what actually happens.

- In **situational irony,** something happens in the story that directly contradicts the expectations of a character or the reader. For example, you would expect that if Jim works hard at his job for a year, he will get a raise. If he gets a pay cut instead, the situation is ironic.
- A **surprise ending** often helps to create situational irony through a turn of events that takes the reader by surprise. To make a surprise ending believable, the author builds clues into the story that make the ending logical.

A. DIRECTIONS: *For each of the following excerpts from "The Gift of the Magi," write* **I** *in the space provided if the excerpt is ironic. Write* **N** *if the excerpt is not ironic. On the lines following each item, briefly explain why the excerpt is or is not ironic.*

____ 1. "Tomorrow would be Christmas Day, and she had only $1.87 with which to buy Jim a present. She had been saving every penny she could for months, with this result."

_____

_____

____ 2. "Where she stopped the sign read: 'Mme. Sofronie. Hair Goods of All Kinds.' One flight up Della ran, and collected herself, panting. Madame, large, too white, chilly, hardly looked the 'Sofronie.'"

_____

_____

____ 3. "Grand as the watch was he sometimes looked at it on the sly on account of the old leather strap that he used in place of a chain."

_____

_____

____ 4. "They were expensive combs, she knew, and her heart had simply craved and yearned over them without the least hope of possession. And now they were hers, but the tresses that should have adorned the coveted adornments were gone."

_____

_____

B. DIRECTIONS: *On the following lines, briefly explain the surprise ending in "The Gift of the Magi." Then, explain how O. Henry makes the surprise ending seem logical.*

_____

_____

_____

_____

Name _____ Date _____

Reading: Use Prior Knowledge and Experience to Make Inferences

An **inference** is an educated guess that you make based on details in a text. In addition to what the author tells you, you can also **use your own prior knowledge and experience** to make inferences.

- As you read, watch movies and plays, and observe the world every day, you gather knowledge and experience.
- When you read something new, look for ways in which the characters and situations resemble ones you have seen before.
- Then, apply that knowledge and experience to make inferences about what you are reading.

Example from "The Gift of the Magi":

Detail from the story: "A furnished flat at $8 per week."

Inference: Della and Jim do not have much money. They have to scrimp and save to get by.

DIRECTIONS: *Use the following chart to record information about the characters listed. Then, make three more inferences about each character based on the details from the story. Some examples are shown.*

Details About Della	Inferences I Can Make About Della
1. She hugs Jim every time he comes home.	Della is deeply in love with her husband.
2. _____ _____	_____ _____
3. _____ _____	_____ _____

Details About Jim	Inferences I Can Make About Jim
1. He greatly values his watch, which was handed down to him.	He has strong feelings for his family.
2. _____ _____	_____ _____
3. _____ _____	_____ _____

"The Gift of the Magi" by O. Henry
Vocabulary Builder

Word List

instigates	depreciate	discreet

A. DIRECTIONS: *Replace each italicized word or group of words with a word from the Word List. Rewrite the sentence in the space provided.*

1. To hide the worn leather strap, Jim takes a *careful* glance at his watch.
   _____

2. For Della, the approaching Christmas holiday *stirs up* a desire to give Jim a special gift.
   _____

3. The beauty of Della's hair is so great that it would *reduce in value* the queen's jewels.
   _____

B. DIRECTIONS: *Decide whether each of the following statements is true or false, and write **T** or **F** on the line provided. Then, explain your answer.*

1. A person who *instigates* conflict might be called a "problem-solver." _____
   _____

2. After 6 years of hard use, a car will *depreciate* in value. _____
   _____

3. Only a *discreet* person should be trusted with a secret. _____
   _____

C. DIRECTIONS: *For each numbered word, choose the word or phrase that is most nearly the same in meaning.*

____ 1. discreet
    A. tactful   **B.** separate   **C.** reckless   **D.** silent

____ 2. instigates
    A. inquires   **B.** calms   **C.** stirs up   **D.** refutes

____ 3. depreciate
    A. criticize   **B.** intensify   **C.** retard   **D.** reduce in value

"The Gift of the Magi" by O. Henry
Support for Writing a News Story

For your brief news story, use the following graphic organizer. Jot down some notes that answer the six questions that reporters ask: *Who? What? When? Where? Why? How?*

Questions	Answers
Who?	
What?	
When?	
Where?	
Why?	
How?	

Use the most important, eye-catching details in your notes to write the lead (opening) paragraph of your human-interest news story on the following lines.

_____

_____

_____

_____

_____

_____

_____

On a separate piece of paper, write your revised lead paragraph and choose other details to write the remaining paragraphs of your story.

"The Gift of the Magi" by O. Henry
Support for Extend Your Learning

Listening and Speaking

Use the following lines to gather information for your debate about the lesson of "The Gift of the Magi." Under each debate position, list some quotations from the story to support that position.

POSITION 1: The story's lesson is that it is foolish to spend money on gifts instead of necessities.

Support for this position:

Example: "Twenty dollars a week doesn't go far. Expenses had been greater than she had calculated. They always are."

_____

_____

POSITION 2: The story's lesson is that sacrifice is the best expression of love.

Support for this position:

Example: "'Will you buy my hair?' asked Della."

_____

_____

Research and Technology

Use the following chart to collect information for your illustrated report about life in New York City or any other large American city around 1905. Keep track of the sources you use for information.

Facts and Details:

1. 'Housing: _____

_____

2. Employment: _____

_____

3. Food: _____

_____

4. Clothing: _____

_____

5. Leisure time/Entertainment: _____

_____

Name _____ Date _____

"The Gift of the Magi" by O. Henry
Enrichment: Calculating Inflation

In "The Gift of the Magi," Jim and Della pay $8.00 a week, or $32.00 a month, to rent their apartment. This price and others quoted in the story reflect the buying power of the dollar in the early 1900s. Today, many people pay more than $800.00 a month to rent an apartment. The increase in the general level of prices of basic goods and services is called *inflation*. In general, as inflation increases, the buying power of the dollar decreases.

DIRECTIONS: *The following chart indicates the price of various items in the years 1906 and 2006. Calculate the percentage of inflation for the hundred-year period and the per-year percentage of inflation. The math calculations are provided in the following example.*

Example:

| Loaf of bread | 1906 price | 2006 price | Price difference |
| | $ .06 | $1.69 | $1.63 |

Calculations:

- [Price difference] $1.63 ÷ Base .06 [1906 price] = 27.17
- 100 [years] × 27.17 = 2717% inflation over 100 years
- 27.17 ÷ 100 years = .2717 = 27.17% inflation per year

Item	Inflation Calculations
1. Woman's dress 1906 cost: $30.00 2006 cost: $100.00	% of inflation over 100 years % of inflation per year
2. One gallon of milk 1906 cost: $ .18 2006 cost: $3.59	% of inflation over 100 years % of inflation per year
3. First-class postage stamp 1906 cost: $ .02 2006 cost: $.37	% of inflation over 100 years % of inflation per year
4. Movie ticket 1906 cost: $ .05 2006 cost: $10.50	% of inflation over 100 years % of inflation per year
5. Automobile (Ford two-door) 1906 cost: $500.00 2006 cost: $19,000	% of inflation over 100 years % of inflation per year

Name _____ Date _____

"The Gift of the Magi" by O. Henry
Selection Test A

Critical Reading *Identify the letter of the choice that best answers the question.*

___ 1. Where and when does "The Gift of the Magi" take place?
   A. an American city in the present
   B. a small town in France around 1900
   C. on the U.S.-Mexican border around 1950
   D. an American city around 1905

___ 2. What is Della's problem in the story?
   A. She wants to buy Jim a gift but has very little money.
   B. She wants to know how to deal with Jim's reactions.
   C. She wants to move to a new apartment but cannot afford it.
   D. She wants to return the watch fob chain she bought for Jim.

___ 3. Which of the following is the best definition of an inference?
   A. a harsh criticism
   B. an educated guess
   C. an accurate retelling
   D. a repetition

___ 4. What does O. Henry mean when he says that "life is made up of sobs, sniffles, and smiles, with sniffles predominating"?
   A. Overall, life is sad.
   B. Della is a crybaby.
   C. People often get sick.
   D. Women express their emotions openly.

___ 5. What inference can you draw about Della from the following passage?
   "Pennies saved one and two at a time by bulldozing the grocer and the vegetable man and the butcher until one's cheeks burned with the silent imputation of parsimony that such close dealing implied."

   A. She was very stingy and hated to go shopping.
   B. She tried to save every cent she could from her very tight budget.
   C. She chose her groceries carefully and enjoyed arguing with the store owners.
   D. She did not like to be overcharged for her groceries.

___ 6. In which of the following items is situational irony best defined?

    A. a contrast between the two leading characters in a story

    B. a contrast between what is expected to happen and what actually happens

    C. a parallel between the beginning of a story and the end

    D. a humorous scene in an otherwise serious story

___ 7. What inference about Jim can you make from details in O. Henry's story?

    A. He is serious and responsible.

    B. He is fun-loving and carefree.

    C. He is proud and standoffish.

    D. He is shy and retiring.

___ 8. When Jim first sees Della's haircut, why does he have a "peculiar expression" on his face?

    A. He is angry with her for cutting her hair.

    B. He is confused about what makes her look different.

    C. He realizes that the combs he bought for her are useless.

    D. He thinks that she is very unattractive.

___ 9. What does Jim's reaction to Della's gift reveal about him?

    A. He is hot-tempered.

    B. He is unappreciative.

    C. He is disapproving.

    D. He is forgiving.

___ 10. How does O. Henry foreshadow the suprise ending in the story?

    A. He describes Della as reckless, so readers are prepared for the sale of her hair.

    B. Della and Jim are so deeply in love that their sacrifice is believable.

    C. Jim has often hinted to Della that he wants a new fob and chain for his watch.

    D. Della has always wanted to try a new hairstyle.

___ 11. Why does O. Henry call Della and Jim wise?

    A. They truly love each other.

    B. They choose gifts that they know the other will like.

    C. They buy gifts that cannot be exchanged.

    D. They buy expensive gifts.

Vocabulary and Grammar

___ 12. Which of the following best defines *discreet* in the sentence from O. Henry's story?

"For ten seconds let us regard with discreet scrutiny some inconsequential object in the other direction."

A. detailed

B. angry

C. tactful

D. patient

___ 13. O. Henry says that Della's hair, before it is cut, would *depreciate* the Queen of Sheba's jewels. Which of the following is the opposite of *depreciate*?

A. reduce in value

B. increase in value

C. evaluate

D. promise

___ 14. Which of the following is the past form of the irregular verb *run*?

A. run

B. running

C. ran

D. runned

___ 15. Which form of the past participle of the irregular verb *give* belongs in the following sentence?

Mme. Sofronie had _____ Della $20.00 for her hair.

A. give

B. gave

C. giving

D. given

Essay

16. In an essay, explain how O. Henry's descriptions of Della and Jim as both foolish and wise can be true, even though that seems like a contradiction. Include details from the story that explain why the two characters are foolish and why they are wise.

17. At the end of the story, Jim's and Della's expectations have been reversed. In an essay, describe the author's use of situational irony in the story. Also, tell how you responded to the surprise ending. What emotions did you feel at the end of the story? How do you think these feelings are related to the story's message?

Name _____ Date _____

"The Gift of the Magi" by O. Henry
Selection Test B

Critical Reading *Identify the letter of the choice that best completes the statement or answers the question.*

____ 1. Which of the following best describes the setting of "The Gift of the Magi"?
A. a small town in southern France in 1900
B. a large American city in the present
C. a small American town in the present
D. a large American city around 1905

____ 2. Which of the following best describes Della's dilemma in this story?
A. how to deal with Jim's reactions
B. how to get money for a gift for Jim
C. how to deal with her unreal expectations
D. how to return the watch fob chain

____ 3. From which statement can you best infer how Jim and Della feel about each other?
A. "Only $1.87 to buy a present for Jim. Her Jim."
B. "'If Jim doesn't kill me,' she said to herself, 'before he takes a second look at me, he'll say I look like a Coney Island chorus girl.'"
C. "Poor fellow, he was only twenty-two—and to be burdened with a family!"
D. "And here I have lamely related to you the uneventful chronicle of two foolish children in a flat who most unwisely sacrificed for each other the greatest treasures of their house."

____ 4. Which of the following best defines an inference?
A. a harsh critique
B. an educated guess
C. an accurate paraphrase
D. an emphatic repetition

____ 5. When O. Henry writes that "life is made up of sobs, sniffles, and smiles, with sniffles predominating," he is making a statement about
A. the overall sadness of life.
B. Della's usually depressed state.
C. how often people become ill.
D. how women freely express emotions.

____ 6. Using prior knowledge and your own experience, what can you infer about Della from the description of her in the following passage?
"Pennies saved one and two at a time by bulldozing the grocer and the vegetable man and the butcher until one's cheeks burned with the silent imputation of parsimony that such close dealing implied."
A. She was stingy to the point of miserliness.
B. By necessity, Della was frugal.
C. She was picky in selecting her groceries.
D. She resented being overcharged for food.

_____ 7. Which of the following is the best definition of situational irony?
   A. an external conflict between the two leading characters in a story
   B. a contrast between what is expected and what actually happens
   C. a parallel situation at the beginning of a story and at the end
   D. a humorous scene in an otherwise predominantly serious story

_____ 8. From details in the story and from your prior knowledge, what inference can you make about Jim's character traits?
   A. He is conscientious and responsible.
   B. He is fun-loving and reckless.
   C. He is proud and arrogant.
   D. He is shy and emotionally withdrawn.

_____ 9. You can infer that Jim's "peculiar expression" when he sees Della's haircut is a result of his
   A. anger with her for cutting her hair without discussing it with him first.
   B. confusion about what makes her look so different.
   C. realization that the combs he bought for her are useless.
   D. loss of physical attraction to her.

_____ 10. What is the irony in O. Henry's description of Madame Sofronie, the hair dealer?
   "Madame, large, too white, chilly, hardly looked the 'Sofronie.'"
   A. Della gets less money for her hair than she had expected.
   B. Madame Sofronie's name leads us to expect elegance, but she looks ordinary instead.
   C. Madame Sofronie has changed so much that Della does not recognize her.
   D. Madame Sofronie speaks little English, so Della has trouble explaining what she wants.

_____ 11. Jim's reaction to Della's gift reveals that he is
   A. hot-tempered.
   B. unappreciative.
   C. disapproving.
   D. forgiving.

_____ 12. Which of the following best explains how O. Henry foreshadows the surprise ending in the story?
   A. Della is characterized as impulsive, so readers are prepared for her selling her hair.
   B. Jim and Della's deep love makes their selling their greatest treasures credible.
   C. Jim has hinted many times to Della that he would appreciate a new watch fob and chain.
   D. For some time, Della has secretly yearned to try a new hairstyle.

_____ 13. O. Henry implies that the reason Della and Jim are wise is because they both choose gifts that
   A. truly express their love.
   B. they know the other would like.
   C. cannot be exchanged.
   D. are worth a lot of money.

Vocabulary and Grammar

___ 14. Which word most closely matches the meaning of *discreet* in the following sentence from "The Gift of the Magi"?

"For ten seconds let us regard with discreet scrutiny some inconsequential object in the other direction."

A. knowledgeable
B. reproachful
C. tactful
D. humiliated

___ 15. In which of the following sentences is the word *instigate* used corectly?

A. Della plans to instigate a surprise gift for Jim.
B. Mme. Sofronie hopes to instigate Della's hair.
C. Della's desire for money leads her to instigate a great change.
D. "Why don't you instigate the chops for supper?" asked Jim.

___ 16. O. Henry says that Della's hair, before it is cut, would *depreciate* the Queen of Sheba's jewels and gifts. Which of the following is closest in meaning to *depreciate*?

A. criticize   B. emphasize   C. compete with   D. reduce in value

___ 17. Which of the following is the past form of the irregular verb *bring*?

A. bringed   B. brang   C. brought   D. brung

___ 18. In which of the following items are the principal parts of the irregular verb *spring* listed correctly?

A. spring, springing, springed, sprang
B. spring, springing, sprang, sprung
C. spring, springing, spranged, sprunged
D. spring, springing, sprang, spranged

Essay

19. At the beginning of the story, descriptive details create a specific picture of Jim and Della's living situation. Write a brief essay in which you explain what that situation is, which key details create that situation, and what inferences you can draw about Della and Jim from your prior knowledge and experience.

20. At the end of the story, Jim's and Della's expectations—as well as the reader's—have been reversed. In an essay, describe and analyze the author's use of situational irony in this tale. Also comment on how you responded to the story's surprise ending. What emotions did this ending create in you, and how are these feelings related to the story's message?

21. O. Henry describes Jim and Della as "two foolish children." He also describes them as the wisest of all who give gifts. In what ways are Jim and Della foolish? In what ways are they wise? How is it possible for them to be both foolish and wise? In an essay, discuss these questions, supporting your responses with references to the story.

Vocabulary Warm-up Word Lists

Study these words from "The Interlopers." Then, complete the activities.

Word List A

assuredly [uh SHOOR id lee] *adv.* certainly; with no doubt
   She is <u>assuredly</u> the best player on the team.

boundary [BOWN duh ree] *n.* border; line that marks the edge of a land area
   We crossed the <u>boundary</u> between the United States and Canada.

disputed [dis PYOO tid] *adj.* being argued about
   They could not agree who owned the <u>disputed</u> baseball.

dramatic [druh MA tik] *adj.* sudden and surprising
   Her <u>dramatic</u> entrance caught everyone's attention.

evident [EV i dent] *adj.* easily noticed or understood
   It was <u>evident</u> from his expression that he did not like the gift.

harbored [HAHR burd] *v.* gave shelter to; was home to
   The forest <u>harbored</u> many small animals.

relationships [ri LAY shuhn ships] *n.* ways people behave toward each other
   They had good <u>relationships</u> with all their neighbors.

restless [REST lis] *adj.* unable to be still
   He was too <u>restless</u> to stay in any one place very long.

Word List B

compromised [KAHM pruh myzd] *v.* settled only when both sides give up something
   They <u>compromised</u> by agreeing to share the prize equally.

distinctly [dis TINKT lee] *adv.* clearly; precisely
   The teacher <u>distinctly</u> explained the assignment so no one would misunderstand.

lawsuit [LAW soot] *n.* problem brought to a court to be settled
   The lawyers met with the judge to discuss the <u>lawsuit</u>.

outlook [OWT look] *n.* view; act of looking out
   My <u>outlook</u> from the mountaintop made me dizzy.

passions [PA shuhnz] *n.* strong emotions or likings
   <u>Passions</u> grew stronger as the day of the big game grew near.

territorial [ter uh TAWR ee uhl] *adj.* relating to land that is owned or controlled
   The nation's <u>territorial</u> claims extended from one coast to the other.

unstrung [un STRUHNG] *adj.* emotionally upset
   She became <u>unstrung</u> by the bad news.

violence [VY uh lens] *n.* strong physical force
   Fighting, shoving, and other forms of <u>violence</u> will not be tolerated.

"The Interlopers" by Saki
Vocabulary Warm-up Exercises

Exercise A *Fill in the blanks using each word from Word List A only once.*

The [1] _____ between members of the Walker and Malone families had

been strained for a long time. It was [2] _____ to everyone who knew them

that the neighbors would never agree on who really owned the [3] _____

land. They had been fighting for years. The Walkers argued that the river formed a natural

[4] _____ between the two properties. The Malones insisted that the wood-

land, which [5] _____ many beautiful songbirds, was rightfully theirs.

Everyone agreed this was [6] _____ a most difficult case. Both families

grew [7] _____ as they waited impatiently for the judge to return with her

ruling. Just then, to their surprise, the door flew open with a bang as the judge made her

[8] _____ entrance into the courtroom. Who would own the land now?

Exercise B *Circle T if the statement is true or F if the statement is false. Then, explain your answer.*

1. If you <u>compromised</u> to reach an agreement, you got everything you wanted.
   T / F _____

2. A <u>lawsuit</u> is usually settled in a theater.
   T / F _____

3. If two candidates have <u>distinctly</u> different views, most people will have trouble
   seeing any difference between them.
   T / F _____

4. Someone on the <u>outlook</u> for signs of a storm is probably watching the sky.
   T / F _____

5. If someone's <u>passions</u> are running high, he or she is probably bored.
   T / F _____

6. A <u>territorial</u> problem is probably of equal interest to people everywhere.
   T / F _____

7. A person who feels <u>unstrung</u> should probably avoid driving a car.
   T / F _____

8. <u>Violence</u> is almost always a good way to settle an argument.
   T / F _____

"The Interlopers" by Saki
Reading Warm-up A

Read the following passage. Pay special attention to the underlined words. Then, read it again, and complete the activities. Use a separate sheet of paper for your written answers.

Everyone gets into arguments sometimes. How do you resolve conflicts with your friends? How do you settle your differences so that no one feels as if he or she lost?

You can deal with conflict in many ways: fight, give in, run away, or use conflict resolution. That is a way of settling arguments so that each person walks away feeling like a winner.

It is <u>assuredly</u> true that some problems are harder to deal with than others. Arguments over <u>disputed</u> property that each side claims as its own can be very difficult to resolve. A disagreement over a <u>boundary</u>, in which two landowners disagree on the border between their properties, often leads to costly legal battles. This might especially be true if the land <u>harbored</u> minerals.

Family <u>relationships</u> between spouses, brothers and sisters, or parents and children often give rise to the most troubling conflicts. Family members may hide bad feelings for a long time before they finally let them surface. People who feel mistreated by a loved one may hold in their resentment for years before suddenly releasing it in a <u>dramatic</u> display of anger. It is <u>evident</u> that hiding one's true feelings is not a good way to settle conflicts.

Arbitration is one type of conflict resolution. People present their case to an impartial arbiter. They agree to accept his or her ruling. In this way, the two parties reach agreement without the high cost of going to court.

Mediation is another tool for bringing people together to work out their problems. Mediators are trained to listen to both sides of a disagreement. They teach people how to listen to one another and work out a solution to their own problems. Anyone who is too <u>restless</u> or too impatient to go through arbitration should first try mediation.

Young people who want to learn more about conflict resolution can get involved in peer mediation programs that may be available in their school system.

1. Underline the words that tell what is <u>assuredly</u> true. Give a synonym for *assuredly*.

2. Underline the words that give a clue to the meaning of <u>disputed</u>. Write a sentence about something you know of that was *disputed*.

3. Circle the word that means about the same thing as <u>boundary</u>. Identify a *boundary* with which you are familiar.

4. Circle the word that tells what could be <u>harbored</u> in the land. Explain the meaning of *harbored*.

5. Underline the words that name people in <u>relationships</u>. Write a sentence about people you know who have close *relationships*.

6. Circle two words that tell what may be released in a <u>dramatic</u> display. Explain how this display might be *dramatic*.

7. Underline the words that tell what is <u>evident</u>. Write a definition of *evident*.

8. Circle the word that means almost the same as <u>restless</u>. What kinds of things make you feel *restless*?

"The Interlopers" by Saki
Reading Warm-up B

Read the following passage. Pay special attention to the underlined words. Then, read it again, and complete the activities. Use a separate sheet of paper for your written answers.

Arthur and Jacob had been best friends since college. Later, when Arthur purchased a house and Jacob was unemployed, Arthur invited his friend to stay in the guest room for a few weeks until he got back on his feet.

After two years, Jacob was still inhabiting the guest room. He had been paying Arthur a minuscule amount of rent, but even those tiny contributions had ceased abruptly almost six months before. Now, Arthur was reluctantly considering filing a <u>lawsuit</u> and letting the courts settle the matter.

"What alternative do I have?" Arthur asked his attorney. "I <u>distinctly</u> recall telling him that the rent is due on the first day of every month."

"What did he say when you asked him for the money?"

"He did not say anything, but he became completely <u>unstrung</u> and looked as if he wanted to hit me! Now I am constantly on the <u>outlook</u> for a punch in the nose!"

"<u>Violence</u> is no way to settle a dispute."

"I agree, especially when it is my nose that is at risk."

"Perhaps if you both give in a little. . . ."

"I tried," said Arthur, "and I even <u>compromised</u> by offering to let him pay me half the money now and the balance of his debt in monthly installments. It seemed like a very generous proposal to me, but Jacob just got angrier when I made the suggestion. Now he is even questioning my <u>territorial</u> rights to the property."

"But it is your house!"

"Of course it is, but Jacob has been living there so long he acts like he owns the place. He is an emotional individual, too. Once his <u>passions</u> take over, he is incapable of engaging in rational discussion."

Just then, Jacob came in and handed Arthur a check.

"Where did all this money come from?" asked Arthur.

"I am sorry," Jacob said sheepishly. "Did I forget to tell you about my night job?"

1. Circle the word that tells where a <u>lawsuit</u> is settled. Why is Arthur planning to file a *lawsuit*?

2. Underline the words that tell what Arthur <u>distinctly</u> recalls doing. Write a sentence about something you can *distinctly* recall telling someone.

3. Underline the words that tell how Jacob looked when he became <u>unstrung</u>. Write about something that might make you become *unstrung*.

4. Write a sentence describing something you might be on the <u>outlook</u> for every day.

5. Are there circumstances that might justify the use of <u>violence</u>? Explain, using a synonym for *violence*.

6. Underline the words that tell how Arthur <u>compromised</u>. Explain what *compromised* means.

7. What does Arthur mean when he says that Jacob questioned his <u>territorial</u> rights?

8. Circle the word that gives a hint to the meaning of <u>passions</u>. Explain why Jacob's *passions* would prevent him from talking rationally.

Name _____ Date _____

Literary Analysis: Irony and Surprise Ending

Irony is a difference or a contradiction between appearance and reality or between what is expected and what actually happens.

- In **situational irony,** something happens in the story that directly contradicts the expectations of a character or the reader. For example, if long-standing enemies suddenly become friends, the situation would be ironic.
- A **surprise ending** often helps to create situational irony through a turn of events that takes the reader by surprise. To make a surprise ending believable, the author builds clues into the story that make the ending logical.

A. DIRECTIONS: *For each of the following excerpts from "The Interlopers," write **I** in the space provided if the excerpt is ironic. Write **N** if the excerpt is not ironic. On the lines following each item, briefly explain why the excerpt is or is not ironic.*

____ 1. If only on this wild night, in this dark, lone spot, he might come across Georg Znaeym, man to man, with one to witness—that was the wish that was uppermost in his thoughts. And as he stepped round the trunk of a huge beech he came face to face with the man he sought.

   _____

   _____

____ 2. Both had now given up the useless struggle to free themselves from the mass of wood that held them down.

   _____

   _____

____ 3. And each prayed a private prayer that his men might be the first to arrive, so that he might be the first to show honorable attention to the enemy that had become a friend.

   _____

   _____

____ 4. The two raised their voices in a prolonged hunting call.

   _____

   _____

B. DIRECTIONS: *On the following lines, briefly explain the surprise ending in "The Interlopers." Then, explain how Saki makes the surprise ending seem logical.*

_____

_____

_____

_____

_____

"The Interlopers" by Saki

Reading: Use Prior Knowledge and Experience to Make Inferences

An **inference** is an educated guess that you make based on details in a text. In addition to what the author tells you, you can also **use your own prior knowledge and experience** to make inferences.

- As you read, watch movies and plays, and observe the world every day, you gather knowledge and experience.
- When you read something new, look for ways in which the characters and situations resemble ones you have seen before.
- Then, apply that knowledge and experience to make inferences about what you are reading.

Example from "The Interlopers":

Detail from the story: "Ulrich von Gradwitz patrolled the dark forest in quest of a human enemy."

Inference: If he finds Georg, Ulrich will try to harm him.

DIRECTIONS: *Use the following chart to record information about the characters listed. Then, make three inferences about each character based on the details from the story. Some examples are shown.*

Details About Ulrich	**Inferences I Can Make About Ulrich**
1. He notices that the roebuck are running in an unusual way.	He is keenly observant.
2. _____	_____
3. _____	_____

Details About Georg	**Inferences I Can Make About Georg**
1. He says he cannot drink wine with an enemy.	He is stubborn and proud.
2. _____	_____
3. _____	_____

"The Interlopers" by Saki
Vocabulary Builder

Word List

precipitous	condolences	languor

A. DIRECTIONS: *Replace each italicized word or group of words with a word from the Word List. Rewrite the sentence in the space provided.*

1. Pinned beneath the huge beech tree, Ulrich experiences pain and *lack of vigor.* _____

   _____

2. Ironically, Georg reassures Ulrich that he will send *expressions of sympathy.* _____

   _____

3. The property in dispute is a narrow strip of *sheer, steeply inclined* woodland. _____

   _____

B. DIRECTIONS: *Revise each sentence so that the underlined vocabulary word is used logically. Be sure to keep the vocabulary word in your revision.*

1. I sent my <u>condolences</u> when I heard that the artist had won a prestigious prize.

   _____

   _____

2. We had an easy half-mile hike over a flat <u>precipitous</u> trail.

   _____

   _____

3. She arises every morning filled with <u>languor</u> and great energy, ready to attack the day.

   _____

   _____

C. DIRECTIONS: *For each numbered word, choose the word or phrase that is most nearly the same in meaning.*

____ 1. condolences
   A. expressions of sympathy   C. shouts of protest
   B. cries of outrage   D. clever replies

____ 2. precipitous
   A. shallow   B. narrow   C. steep   D. rough

____ 3. languor
   A. tardiness   B. weakness   C. gentleness   D. coarseness

"The Interlopers" by Saki
Support for Writing a News Story

To gather information for your brief news story about Ulrich and Georg, use the following graphic organizer. Jot down some notes that answer the six questions that reporters ask: *Who? What? When? Where? Why? How?*

Questions	Answers
Who?	
What?	
When?	
Where?	
Why?	
How?	

Use the most important, eye-catching details in your notes to write the lead (opening) paragraph of your human-interest news story on the following lines.

_____

_____

_____

_____

_____

_____

On a separate piece of paper, write your revised lead paragraph and choose other details to write the remaining paragraphs of your story.

"The Interlopers" by Saki
Support for Extend Your Learning

Listening and Speaking

Use the following lines to gather information for your debate about the disputed land in "The Interlopers." Under each debate position, list two reasons or quotations from the story to explain why the character is entitled to the land. One reason has been given as an example.

POSITION 1: Ulrich von Gradwitz is entitled to the disputed land.

Support for this position:

Example: In the lawsuit, the court ruled that the Znaeym family had taken illegal possession.

_____

_____

POSITION 2: Georg Znaeym is entitled to the disputed land.

Support for this position:

Example: The court's judgment in the lawsuit was improper.

_____

_____

Research and Technology

Use the following chart to collect information for your presentation about the danger of wolves. Keep track of the sources you use for information.

Facts and Details:

1. Physical description: _____

_____

2. Where they live: _____

_____

3. What they eat: _____

_____

4. Encounters with humans: _____

_____

5. Danger to humans: Myth or reality? _____

_____

Possible Illustrations:

_____

_____

"The Interlopers" by Saki

Enrichment: Problem Solving

Of all the skills you will learn before entering the working world, problem solving and conflict resolution are among the most essential. Whether you are working at an office or a hospital, a restaurant or a school, a retail store or a construction site, you will undoubtedly encounter unique sets of problems and conflicts that need to be solved. Being able to recognize and solve problems will help you work with others and be more effective at your job. The following chart outlines the basic steps to problem solving.

DIRECTIONS: *Imagine that Ulrich and Georg in "The Interlopers" survive their experiences in the forest and have the chance to resolve completely the conflict between their families. Using your imagination and details from the story, fill in the following chart to show how they might use problem-solving steps effectively. The first two steps have been provided for you as examples.*

Steps to Problem Solving	Specific Steps Taken by Ulrich and Georg
1. Recognize that a problem exists (identify a difference between what is and what could or should be).	Ulrich and Georg have wasted their lives fighting. They realize that the bitterness between their families has become destructive.
2. Identify possible reasons for the problem.	Greed, disrespect, and an unwillingness to compromise are causes of the problem.
3. Devise and implement a plan to solve the problem.	_____ _____ _____
4. Evaluate and monitor the progress of the resolution.	_____ _____
5. Revise the plan as indicated by findings.	_____ _____

"The Gift of the Magi" by O. Henry

"The Interlopers" by Saki

Build Language Skills: Vocabulary

Word Roots

The Latin root *-mot-* means "to move." This root is contained in the word *motivate*, which means "causing someone or something to move or act," and also in *motive*, which means "the reason that someone or something acts." *Motivation* is the feeling of wanting to move or act.

Example: Ulrich's anger toward Georg motivated him to patrol the forest.

A. DIRECTIONS: *Use a dictionary to look up the origin of each of the following words containing the root -mot-. Write one meaning for each word. Then, write a sentence in which you use the word in a context that makes its meaning clear.*

1. remote   Meaning: _____

   Sentence: _____

2. emotion   Meaning: _____

   Sentence: _____

3. commotion   Meaning: _____

   Sentence: _____

4. promotion   Meaning: _____

   Sentence: _____

Academic Vocabulary Practice

B. DIRECTIONS: *Follow the instructions to write sentences containing the Academic Vocabulary words.*

1. Use *emotion* in a sentence about a newspaper editorial.

   _____

2. Use *motive* in a sentence about a detective thriller.

   _____

3. Use *circumstance* in a sentence about the verdict of a jury at a criminal trial.

   _____

4. Use *categorize* in a sentence about animal species.

   _____

5. Use *aspect* in a sentence about a reaction to a movie.

   _____

Name _____ Date _____

Build Language Skills: Grammar

Irregular Verbs

Unlike regular verbs, the past tense and past participle of **irregular verbs** are not formed by adding *-ed* or *-d* to the present form. Instead, the past tense and past participle are formed in various ways. In some verbs, there is a change of vowels or consonants within the word. Other verbs change both vowels and consonants. Sometimes, the past and the past participle of an irregular verb are identical. In some irregular verbs, though, the past and the past participle have different forms.

Study the forms of the irregular verbs shown in the following chart.

Principal Parts of Irregular Verbs

Present	Present Participle	Past	Past Participle
run	(is) running	ran	(has) run
catch	(is) catching	caught	(has) caught
sit	(is) sitting	sat	(has) sat
fall	(is) falling	fell	(has) fallen
take	(is) taking	took	(has) taken

A. PRACTICE: *On the line provided, write the correct form of the verb in parentheses.*

1. Jim did not know that Della had (selled, sold) her hair.

   _____

2. If you had met Ulrich in the forest, would you have (ran, run) away?

   _____

3. The feud between Ulrich's and Georg's families (began, begun) long ago with a land dispute.

   _____

B. Writing Application: *Read the following sentences and notice the verbs in italics. If the verb is used correctly, write Correct in the space provided. If the verb is not used correctly, rewrite the sentence using the correct form.*

1. Although Saki wrote history, novels, and political satire, he is *knowed* especially for his short stories.

   _____

2. Born in Burma as H. H. Munro, he was *bringed* up in England by two aunts.

   _____

3. As a foreign correspondent, he *spended* time in Poland, Russia, and Paris.

   _____

79

Name _____ Date _____

Critical Reading *Identify the letter of the choice that best answers the question.*

____ 1. Which of the following best describes the overall message of "The Interlopers"?
   A. Bitter quarrels are foolish.
   B. The woods can be dangerous in winter.
   C. Hunting is an exciting pastime.
   D. Friendship has many benefits.

____ 2. How would you describe the mood, or atmosphere, at the beginning of "The Interlopers"?
   A. dark and foreboding
   B. desperate and anxious
   C. light and cheerful
   D. horrible and frightening

____ 3. What inference can you make about Ulrich at the beginning of the story?
   A. He is excited and eager for the hunt.
   B. He is afraid and wants to end the feud.
   C. He is upset at being out in the cold.
   D. He is angry and hopes to find his enemy.

____ 4. In "The Interlopers," why does Ulrich go into the woods on the night of the story?
   A. He hopes to find Georg and make peace.
   B. He needs to go hunting for food.
   C. He suspects that Georg is poaching in the forest.
   D. He wants to drive the wolves away from his land.

____ 5. In Saki's story, both men had expected to fight each other. Instead, the two men are pinned by a huge fallen tree. Which literary term best describes this change in situation?
   A. flashback
   B. foreshadowing
   C. irony
   D. metaphor

____ 6. When Ulrich offers Georg a drink from his wine flask, what inference can you make about Ulrich's attitude?

    A. He has totally given up hope of their being rescued.

    B. He is trying to trick Georg.

    C. He doesn't care if Georg accepts his offer.

    D. He is beginning to feel more friendly toward Georg.

____ 7. What causes Ulrich to cry out in joy?

    A. the drink of wine

    B. Georg's offer of hospitality

    C. making peace with Georg

    D. the figures coming down the hill

____ 8. Why might the following passage from "The Interlopers" be considered ironic?

    "'How many of them are there?' asked Georg.

    'I can't see distinctly,' said Ulrich; 'nine or ten.'

    'Then they are yours,' said Georg; 'I had only seven out with me.'

    'They are making all the speed they can, brave lads,' said Ulrich gladly."

    A. Ulrich has counted the figures incorrectly.

    B. Georg regrets that his men have not kept up with him.

    C. The men mistakenly assume that the figures are human.

    D. Ulrich and Georg are in such pain that they have trouble communicating.

____ 9. What makes the ending of "The Interlopers" surprising?

    A. Despite the two men's efforts, the feud will continue.

    B. The two men are trapped by a tree they both claim to own.

    C. The figures in the woods are not what they appear to be.

    D. Ulrich laughs at the danger the two men face.

____ 10. How do Ulrich's and Georg's feelings toward each other change during the story?

    A. from dislike to gratitude

    B. from hatred to friendship

    C. from disregard to respect

    D. from disrespect to hatred

____ 11. Which of the following best describes the tone at the end of Saki's story?

    A. grateful

    B. grim

    C. cheerful

    D. sympathetic

Vocabulary and Grammar

_____ **12.** In which of the following sentences is the word *condolences* used correctly?

   A. After she won the race, she accepted our condolences.

   B. We sent Tina our condolences on her grandmother's death.

   C. Condolences from our whole family on the opening of your new restaurant!

   D. Can we buy condolences at this store?

_____ **13.** Which word best describes the weakness felt by Ulrich and Georg after they have been pinned by the tree?

   A. agility

   B. resilience

   C. curiosity

   D. languor

_____ **14.** Which of the following is the correct past participle of the irregular verb *ring*?

   A. ringing

   B. ringed

   C. rung

   D. rang

_____ **15.** In which of the following items are the principal parts of the verb *win* listed correctly?

   A. win, winning, won, won

   B. win, winning, winned, won

   C. win, winning, won, wun

   D. win, winning, winned, winned

Essay

16. What makes the ending of "The Interlopers" surprising? Has the author prepared you for the ending, or were you led to expect a different kind of ending? In an essay, answer these questions, using evidence from the story as support.

17. In an essay, describe how "Nature's own violence" overwhelms the men in "The Interlopers." Why do you suppose Saki chose to have nature destroy the men rather than have the men destroy each other?

"The Interlopers" by Saki
Selection Test B

Critical Reading *Identify the letter of the choice that best completes the statement or answers the question.*

____ 1. The main lesson in "The Interlopers" concerns the
A. foolishness of petty quarrels.
B. danger of the winter woods.
C. excitement of hunting.
D. benefits of friendship.

____ 2. What inference can you make about Ulrich's state of mind at the beginning of the story?
A. He is excited and eager for the hunt to begin.
B. He is relaxed and hopes to reconcile with his enemy.
C. He is upset at freezing in the woods and eager to get home.
D. He is vengeful and hopes to find his enemy.

____ 3. What prompts Ulrich to go into the woods on the night of the story?
A. He hopes to find Georg and reconcile their differences.
B. He needs to go hunting for food.
C. He suspects that Georg will be poaching in the forest.
D. He wants to drive the wolves away from his land.

____ 4. Based on your prior knowledge and experience, what can you infer about Ulrich's motive for straying away from his foresters on the night he finds Georg in the woods?
A. He thinks he hears footsteps and follows the sound.
B. He wants to be alone to think about his problems.
C. He wants no witnesses to what he plans to do.
D. He is searching for the huge, fallen beech tree.

____ 5. In "The Interlopers," both men had expected to fight one another. Instead, they struggle to free themselves from a huge fallen tree that pins them to the ground. Which literary term best describes this sudden reversal?
A. hyperbole
B. symbolism
C. foreshadowing
D. irony

____ 6. Georg's elaborate description of the two men's new life as friends might be regarded as ironic because
A. such a reversal in their relationship is totally unexpected.
B. few of the villagers will believe that their friendship is sincere.
C. their friendship will probably not last, given the pressures of the feuding families.
D. Georg is trying to lull Ulrich into a false sense of security.

____ 7. In "The Interlopers," what causes Ulrich to utter a cry of joy?
A. a draft of wine
B. Georg's offer of hospitality
C. the reconciliation with Georg
D. the figures hurrying toward them

_____ 8. How do Ulrich's and Georg's feelings toward each other change during the story?
  A. from friendship to suspicion
  B. from hatred to friendship
  C. from respect to disrespect
  D. from sympathy to hatred

_____ 9. Why might the following excerpt from the dialogue in Saki's story be considered ironic?
  "'How many of them are there?' asked Georg.
  'I can't see distinctly,' said Ulrich; 'nine or ten.'
  'Then they are yours,' said Georg; 'I had only seven out with me.'
  'They are making all the speed they can, brave lads,' said Ulrich gladly."
  A. Ulrich has counted the figures incorrectly; there are many more than nine or ten.
  B. Georg regrets that his men have not come to their aid much sooner.
  C. The men's assumption that the figures are human is incorrect.
  D. Because of their intense pain, Ulrich and Georg have trouble communicating.

_____ 10. What makes the resolution of Saki's story surprising?
  A. Despite Ulrich and Georg's reconciliation, it seems that their feud will continue.
  B. The two men are trapped by a tree they both claim to own.
  C. The approaching figures in the woods are not what they appear to be.
  D. Ulrich laughs at the danger the two men face.

_____ 11. At the end of Saki's story, to which of the following might you apply the word *interlopers* from the title?
  A. Ulrich's men
  B. Georg's men
  C. Ulrich and Georg
  D. the wolves

_____ 12. Which of the following best describes the tone at the end of "The Interlopers"?
  A. appreciative
  B. grim
  C. festive
  D. philosophical

Vocabulary and Grammar

_____ 13. An appropriate word to describe the the steep, sheer woodlands in which Ulrich encounters Georg is
  A. precipitous.   C. shady.
  B. tropical.   D. parched.

_____ 14. Which word best describes the weakness felt by Ulrich and Georg after they have been pinned under the tree for some time?
  A. agility   C. congeniality
  B. resilience   D. languor

_____ 15. Which of the following is the past participle of the irregular verb *begin*?
  A. beginned
  B. beginning
  C. began
  D. begun

_____ 16. Which of the following is the past participle of the irregular verb *lead*?
  A. lead
  B. laid
  C. led
  D. leaded

_____ 17. In which of the following items are the principal parts of the verb *put* listed correctly?
  A. put, putting, put, put
  B. put, putting, putted, putted
  C. put, putting, putten, putten
  D. put, putting, pat, put

Essay

18. In "The Interlopers," a violent storm causes a tree to fall on longtime enemies Georg and Ulrich. As a result, the men are caught beneath the tree and fear that their lives are in serious danger. How does this situation cause the men to rethink life and their bitter feud, and why is the change in their outlook ironic? What further ironic twist occurs at the end of the story? In a brief essay, explain your answers to these questions.

19. At the beginning of "The Interlopers," Saki writes that before Georg or Ulrich has a chance to act on his hatred for the other, "Nature's own violence overwhelmed them both." In an essay, describe how "Nature's own violence" overwhelms the men at this point in the story and also at the end of the tale. Why might Saki have chosen to have nature destroy the men rather than have the men destroy themselves? What message might the author be conveying about the role of nature and the role of human plans and wishes?

20. The word *interlopers* can be defined as those who intrude on the affairs of others. What are three possible interpretations of the story's title? In an essay, explain these interpretations, using details from the story.

Vocabulary Warm-up Word Lists

Study these words from the stories. Then, complete the activities.

Word List A

ceremonial [ser uh MOH nee uhl] *adj.* used or done in a ceremony
   The museum displayed a <u>ceremonial</u> gown worn for special occasions.

cheekbones [CHEEK bohnz] *n.* bones on the face just below the eyes
   The boxer's <u>cheekbones</u> were broken in the fight.

ensure [en SHOOR] *v.* to make sure or certain
   To <u>ensure</u> our money is safe, I will keep it in a locked box.

glossy [GLAW see] *adj.* having a smooth and shiny surface
   The actor made <u>glossy</u> photos of himself to sign and give to fans.

penetrated [PEN uh tray tid] *v.* entered or passed through
   Water from the leaky pipe <u>penetrated</u> the ceiling and left a stain.

scuffed [SKUHFD] *adj.* showing marks or scrapes from wear
   Noah's new shoes were <u>scuffed</u> and dirty from running.

sundown [SUHN down] *n.* time of day when the sun sets
   Let's take a swim at <u>sundown</u> before it is completely dark.

wilted [WIL tid] *adj.* looking droopy or shriveled
   Her disappointment at the news was reflected in her <u>wilted</u> smile.

Word List B

continuous [kuhn TIN yoo us] *adj.* happening or existing without pausing
   The seasons change in a <u>continuous</u> cycle, year after year.

exhibited [eg ZIB i tid] *v.* showed a quality, a sign, or an emotion easily noticed
   She <u>exhibited</u> her independent streak by insisting on going alone.

historical [his TAW ruh kuhl] *adj.* relating to the study of history
   My knowledge of <u>historical</u> events is limited to American history.

imperative [im PER uh tiv] *adj.* absolutely necessary; urgent
   It is <u>imperative</u> that we get to the airport before the flight lands.

judgment [JUHJ ment] *n.* ability to decide wisely; opinion
   Our court system depends on the clear thinking and <u>judgment</u> of a jury of our peers.

mystified [MIS tuh fyd] *adj.* confused; unable to understand
   Even the doctors were <u>mystified</u> by my strange symptoms.

nightfall [NYT fawl] *n.* end of daylight; dusk
   I like to watch the buildings in the city light up at <u>nightfall</u>.

portions [POHR shuhnz] *n.* parts of something larger
   <u>Portions</u> of the roof were damaged, but most of it is okay.

"The Man to Send Rain Clouds" by Leslie Marmon Silko
"Old Man of the Temple" by R. K. Narayan
Vocabulary Warm-up Exercises

Exercise A *Fill in the blanks using each word from Word List A only once.*

Where I live by a lake, it is tradition to have a [1] _____ good-bye to summer. We hold a picnic for all of the families around us to [2] _____ that no one feels left out. By then, many of our faces are deeply colored on our noses and [3] _____ from days in the sun. [4] _____ sandals are evidence of vacation fun and games. There may also be [5] _____ plants in the garden, now past their summer prime, and even a slight chill of autumn that has [6] _____ the air. When the [7] _____ surface of the lake reflects the last pink clouds after [8] _____, we know that it is time to pack up our picnic and say farewell until next year.

Exercise B *Answer the questions with complete explanations.*

Example: How would you expect a friend to respond if you said it was <u>imperative</u> that you meet?
> *I would expect the friend to see me immediately because <u>imperative</u> means "urgent," so I would be asking for a meeting right away.*

1. If you were in <u>continuous</u> pain and did not know the cause, what should you do?
_____

2. What typical daily activities might you be doing at <u>nightfall</u>?
_____

3. If <u>portions</u> of a bridge were washed away by a flood, could you still cross the bridge?
_____

4. If someone <u>exhibited</u> good <u>judgment</u> in choosing friends, what could you learn from that person?
_____

5. Would a <u>historical</u> movie ever be set in the future?
_____

6. What kind of situation would you be in if you were <u>mystified</u> by a problem?
_____

"The Man to Send Rain Clouds" by Leslie Marmon Silko
"Old Man of the Temple" by R. K. Narayan
Reading Warm-up A

Read the following passage. Pay special attention to the underlined words. Then, read it again, and complete the activities. Use a separate sheet of paper for your written answers.

Ray trailed behind his father up the dense, steep slope. He slipped on a patch of wet leaves and stumbled. If only he could see better! The sunlight <u>penetrated</u> only where the trees were not too thick. In one spot where the light passed through, he frowned as he looked down at his almost-new sneakers that were now <u>scuffed</u>. Look at those marks! He knew he should have worn his old pair. Even more, he knew he should have said "no" to his father this year.

When Joseph, Ray's father, heard the crashing sound, he stopped to be sure his son was okay. As a gentle smile creased Joseph's face, his high <u>cheekbones</u> rose even higher. Ray was growing so fast that he was all left feet—just as Joseph had been at Ray's age.

Back on the trail, the two continued toward the flat ridge above. Here and there, Joseph picked <u>wilted</u> plants that might look shriveled but which he knew could still be brewed for the herbal teas he enjoyed.

The day was fading and <u>sundown</u> was near when they reached the ridge. Ray quickly helped find wood for a fire. The pit was lined with large, round stones to <u>ensure</u> that the fire would not spread. Ray knew his father always made certain that the flames could not get out of control.

Ray pulled out a <u>glossy</u> sports magazine while his father made dinner, and the shiny cover sparkled in the firelight. Soon, his father's cooking drew his attention. The food was delicious; Ray felt quite contented.

At the traditional hour, Joseph placed more wood on the fire until it leapt high into the air. Then he sang a song of his ancestors that came from deep within. Ray listened to the melody floating up to the stars. From the high ridge, he could see more fires like theirs, <u>ceremonial</u> blazes set to thank nature for a bountiful fall. Each year Ray complained about the long hike, but each year found him on top of the ridge, joining his father in the ancient song.

1. Underline the words that give a clue to the meaning of <u>penetrated</u>. What blocked the sunlight so that it *penetrated* only in places?

2. Circle the word that gives a clue to the meaning of <u>scuffed</u>. Why is Ray upset about his *scuffed* sneakers?

3. Circle the word that explains where <u>cheekbones</u> are located. Underline the adjective that describes Joseph's *cheekbones*.

4. Circle the word that is a clue to <u>wilted</u>. Give an antonym for *wilted* in this passage.

5. Circle the words that are clues to the meaning of <u>sundown</u>. Explain why Ray needed to move quickly when it was almost *sundown*.

6. Circle words that give a clue to the meaning of <u>ensure</u>. Underline what was done to *ensure* that the fire would not spread.

7. Circle the clue to <u>glossy</u>. How would you describe a *glossy* magazine?

8. Underline the purpose of the <u>ceremonial</u> fire. What kind of tradition do you think this might be?

"The Man to Send Rain Clouds" by Leslie Marmon Silko
"Old Man of the Temple" by R. K. Narayan

Reading Warm-up B

Read the following passage. Pay special attention to the underlined words. Then, read it again, and complete the activities. Use a separate sheet of paper for your written answers.

The cycle of life is a <u>continuous</u> one. People are born and people die every day. It is not surprising, then, that many traditions have developed around this cycle, and especially death. Beliefs concerning the dead are part of virtually every culture. They have been <u>exhibited</u> since ancient times in burial rituals, customs, and holidays.

Looking through the pages of history, we can find plenty of evidence of these beliefs. Some of it is still clearly seen today, as in the colossal pyramids of Egypt. We may be <u>mystified</u> at how workers without modern tools created those enormous stone structures. However, thanks to archaeologists and other <u>historical</u> experts, there is no confusion about why the pyramids were built. They served as tombs for the pharaohs.

Honoring those who have died is <u>imperative</u> for many peoples. This urgent need has given rise to both solemn and festive occasions in many cultures. In Mexico, a yearly celebration known as the Day of the Dead is thousands of years old. On the first two days of November, graves of relatives are decorated with special foods and flowers. Parades are held and bonfires are set at <u>nightfall</u> to light the dark. At family reunions, people celebrate the memory of loved ones who have died.

Some cultures have had what may be viewed as unusual rituals. Aborigines, the native peoples of Australia, had the tradition of placing the dead in trees. In the Solomon Islands, the deceased were taken to reefs in the ocean, to be consumed by sharks. Most scholars who study such traditions work to be objective. They do not pass <u>judgment</u> on whether a particular custom is "right" or "wrong." The diversity of cultures on the planet ensures that in <u>portions</u> of the world, certain sets of beliefs will be followed, while in other parts of the world, customs and beliefs will take a different form. What links people everywhere are life's common experiences, such as birth and death.

1. Underline the sentence that describes the <u>continuous</u> cycle of life. Give a synonym for *continuous*.

2. Underline what the passage says is <u>exhibited</u> through customs and traditions. Describe a tradition at your school and how it is *exhibited*.

3. Circle the word that is a clue to <u>mystified</u>. Underline what the passage says has *mystified* people about the pyramids.

4. What kind of knowledge do <u>historical</u> experts need? Underline the word for *historical* experts who study objects from ancient cultures.

5. Circle words that are clues to <u>imperative</u>. Describe something that is *imperative* for a student to do, and why.

6. Circle the word that is a clue to <u>nightfall</u>. What is the opposite time of day?

7. Underline the phrase that explains what <u>judgment</u> most scholars do not make. Is a *judgment* a fact or an opinion? Explain.

8. Circle the word that is a clue to <u>portions</u>. Give a synonym for *portions*.

"The Man to Send Rain Clouds" by Leslie Marmon Silko
"Old Man of the Temple" by R. K. Narayan
Literary Analysis: Setting

The **setting** of a story is the time and place in which it occurs.

- The time may include not only the historical period but also a specific year, season, and hour of day.
- Place may involve not only geographical location but also the social, economic, and cultural environment.

The importance of setting varies from story to story.

- Sometimes, the setting simply furnishes a backdrop for the action. In such a story, the setting could change, but the characters, actions, and events would remain the same.
- Alternatively, the setting can shape the characters and events. For example, in a story set within a Native American culture, characters may make specific decisions and choices based on the rituals and expectations of the culture.
- Setting can play an important role in establishing or intensifying the atmosphere or over-all mood in a story.

DIRECTIONS: *As you read these stories, concentrate on the specific details about setting. List some of these details, and then describe why they are important to the story.*

"The Man to Send Rain Clouds"

1. Details of characters' physical surroundings: _____
_____

2. Details that reflect the time in which the story takes place: _____
_____

3. Details that reflect the characters' culture: _____
_____

4. Overall importance of setting in the story: _____
_____

"Old Man of the Temple"

5. Details of characters' physical surroundings: _____
_____

6. Details that reflect the time in which the story takes place: _____
_____

7. Details that reflect the characters' culture: _____
_____

8. Overall importance of setting: _____
_____

"The Man to Send Rain Clouds" by Leslie Marmon Silko
"Old Man of the Temple" by R. K. Narayan
Vocabulary Builder

Word List

penetrated	perverse	awry	venture

A. DIRECTIONS: *Revise each sentence so that the underlined vocabulary word is used logically. Be sure not to change the vocabulary word.*

1. His determination to break school rules is so <u>perverse</u> that the principal sent him a note of congratulations.

   _____

   _____

2. He was really happy when he discovered that his well-laid plans had gone <u>awry</u>.

   _____

   _____

3. When we saw how promptly they had taken their seats, we were impressed by their <u>venture</u>.

   _____

   _____

4. Her winter jacket is so well lined that the bitingly cold wind <u>penetrated</u> it easily.

   _____

   _____

B. DIRECTIONS: *Write the letter of the word or phrase that is the best antonym (word that means the opposite) for the Word List word.*

___ 1. perverse
    A. beneficial
    B. harmful
    C. useful
    D. ridiculous

___ 2. venture
    A. any action
    B. risky action
    C. safe action
    D. useless action

___ 3. awry
    A. crooked
    B. straight
    C. disastrous
    D. enormous

___ 4. penetrated
    A. went through
    B. did not go through
    C. acted carelessly
    D. carefully prepared

"The Man to Send Rain Clouds" by Leslie Marmon Silko
"Old Man of the Temple" by R. K. Narayan
Writing to Compare Literary Works

Use this chart to take prewriting notes for your essay comparing and contrasting the way the setting of each story influences the characters and story events.

Points of Comparison/Contrast	"The Man to Send Rain Clouds"	"Old Man of the Temple"
Daily lives of characters		
Cultural values and beliefs		
Effects of setting on characters		

"The Man to Send Rain Clouds" by Leslie Marmon Silko
"Old Man of the Temple" by R. K. Narayan
Selection Test A

Critical Reading *Identify the letter of the choice that best answers the question.*

____ 1. What is the setting of "The Man to Send Rain Clouds"?
  A. Illinois
  B. Nevada
  C. California
  D. New Mexico

____ 2. Who is Teofilo in "The Man to Send Rain Clouds"?
  A. a Roman Catholic missionary
  B. Louise's son
  C. an old Pueblo Indian who has died before the story opens
  D. the leader of the Pueblo community

____ 3. In "The Man to Send Rain Clouds," why is the cultural setting important?
  A. It provides a context for the main conflict in the story.
  B. It allows the author to write beautiful descriptions of the landscape.
  C. It explains the goals of Father Paul in his missionary work.
  D. It gives the reader insight into the personal beliefs of Teofilo.

____ 4. Which is the most important reason that Father Paul refuses at first to bring holy water to the grave in "The Man to Send Rain Clouds"?
  A. He is afraid he will not be welcome.
  B. He has not performed the Last Rites.
  C. He is angry that Leon and Ken did not tell him the full truth.
  D. He does not hold funeral masses for Pueblo Indians.

____ 5. Which sentence from "The Man to Send Rain Clouds" creates an image that appeals to the sense of touch?
  A. Leon turned to look up at the high blue mountains in the deep snow. . . .
  B. The priest stared down at his scuffed brown loafers and the worn hem of his cassock.
  C. His fingers were stiff, and it took him a long time to twist the lid off the holy water.
  D. Leon stared at the new moccasins that Teofilo had made for the ceremonial dances. . . .

_____ 6. At the end of "The Man to Send Rain Clouds," what does Leon's reaction to the sprinkling of the holy water suggest?

   A. Leon cannot understand Roman Catholic rituals.

   B. For Leon, the holy water symbolizes rain clouds.

   C. Leon feels he has made a mistake by inviting Father Paul to the graveside.

   D. Leon feels that Teofilo has lived his life in vain.

_____ 7. What is the setting of "Old Man of the Temple"?

   A. inside a large Buddhist temple in Thailand at sunset

   B. near a ruined Hindu temple by the side of the road in South India late at night

   C. in the imperial gardens in Tokyo, Japan, late at night in early spring

   D. near an ancient temple in China at noon

_____ 8. At the opening of "Old Man of the Temple," how does the narrator describe Doss, his driver?

   A. as well-behaved and obedient

   B. as irritable and impatient

   C. as unreliable and disobedient

   D. as humble and intelligent

_____ 9. In "Old Man of the Temple," who has been knocking on the family's door?

   A. the ghost of Seetha

   B. the ghost of the king

   C. the ghost of Krishna Battar

   D. Doss

_____ 10. In which selection(s) does the setting contain elements of fantasy?

   A. in "The Man to Send Rain Clouds"

   B. in "Old Man of the Temple"

   C. in both selections

   D. in neither selection

_____ 11. Which statement most accurately contrasts the settings of "The Man to Send Rain Clouds" and "Old Man of the Temple"?

   A. One story has a definite setting; the other does not.

   B. One story takes place in the present; the other is set in eighteenth-century India.

   C. One story takes place in New Mexico; the other is set in California.

   D. One story has a totally realistic setting; the other has an element of fantasy.

_____ 12. Which statement is true of both "The Man to Send Rain Clouds" and "Old Man of the Temple"?
   A. Both stories are about mysterious, horrifying events.
   B. Both stories are about ordinary events of everyday life.
   C. Both stories have to do with a culture's beliefs about death.
   D. Both stories describe a way of life that existed hundreds of years ago.

Vocabulary

_____ 13. Which of the following could fairly be called <u>perverse</u>?
   A. complaining unreasonably about a disappointment
   B. insisting on doing what is wrong or harmful
   C. arguing strongly for one's own point of view
   D. obeying exactly all rules and laws

_____ 14. If you hang a picture <u>awry</u>, how will it look?
   A. colorful
   B. symmetrical
   C. appropriate
   D. crooked

Essay

15. In "The Man to Send Rain Clouds," the author bases the story's main conflict on cultural differences that relate to the setting. In "Old Man of the Temple," some beliefs of Hinduism, the major religion of India, furnish an important background for the story. In an essay, discuss how the cultural environment is an important part of the setting in both stories.

16. Choose either "The Man to Send Rain Clouds" or "Old Man of the Temple." Write an essay analyzing the author's portrayal of the main character. (Write about Leon in "The Man to Send Rain Clouds" or the narrator in "Old Man of the Temple.") In your essay, identify two personality traits of the character you choose. For each trait, give one example of how the character shows that trait in the story.

"The Man to Send Rain Clouds" by Leslie Marmon Silko
"Old Man of the Temple" by R. K. Narayan
Selection Test B

Critical Reading *Identify the letter of the choice that best completes the statement or answers the question.*

____ 1. Several details in "The Man to Send Rain Clouds" make it clear that the story is set in
    A. the Midwest.
    B. the Pacific Northwest.
    C. the Southwest.
    D. California.

____ 2. In "The Man to Send Rain Clouds," we can infer from Leon's and Ken's responses to finding Teofilo that the Pubelo Indians view death with
    A. joy.
    B. sadness.
    C. acceptance.
    D. anger.

____ 3. In Silko's story, the conflict between the Pueblo and Christian cultures is evident when
    A. Leon tells Father Paul that the Last Rites were not necessary.
    B. Leon dresses Teofilo in a new brown flannel shirt and new jeans.
    C. Father Paul welcomes Leon into his house.
    D. Father Paul and Leon walk together to the graveyard.

____ 4. Which is the most important example of the cultural setting in "The Man to Send Rain Clouds"?
    A. the candles and medicine bags of the old men
    B. the brass lamp that hangs in Father Paul's living room
    C. the missionary magazine that Father Paul reads
    D. the pickup truck that Leon and Ken drive out to the sheep camp

____ 5. Which statement reflects Father Paul's relationship with the Pueblos?
    A. Both sides are eager to meet each other halfway.
    B. There is complete understanding between Father Paul and the Pueblos.
    C. It is a relationship marked by great tension and extreme hostility.
    D. The relationship is rarely close and often difficult.

____ 6. In what way are the Christian and Pueblo people in "The Man to Send Rain Clouds" alike?
    A. Both have special ceremonies for the dead.
    B. Both have rejected the past.
    C. Each accepts the beliefs of the other.
    D. Both are concerned about the weather.

____ 7. Where does the action in "Old Man of the Temple" take place?
    A. in Thailand
    B. in India
    C. in Indonesia
    D. in Vietnam

___ 8. What is the main conflict in "Old Man of the Temple"?

    A. an external conflict between Doss and the old man

    B. an internal conflict between the old man and his memories

    C. an external conflict between the narrator and the old man

    D. an internal conflict between the narrator and his conscience

___ 9. When Doss speaks in a "thin, piping voice" in "Old Man of the Temple," it is because

    A. Doss has been frightened by the old man.

    B. Doss has been transformed into the old man.

    C. Doss has had too much to drink.

    D. Doss feels deliriously happy.

___ 10. Which of the following is an important cultural factor in "Old Man of the Temple"?

    A. a set of religious beliefs in reincarnation and the transfer of souls into other bodies

    B. a group of myths stressing the eternal conflict between good and evil

    C. a set of religious beliefs that prohibits injury to any living thing

    D. a collection of folk tales centering on a particular temple

___ 11. Why may "Old Man of the Temple" be classified as a fantasy?

    A. because the story is unpredictable

    B. because the action is set in an exotic location

    C. because the story contains elements that could not really happen

    D. because the action takes place near an ancient temple

___ 12. Which statement most accurately describes Silko's and Narayan's stories?

    A. Both stories predict future events.

    B. Both stories deal with beliefs about death.

    C. Both stories deal with violent conflicts.

    D. Setting is unimportant in both stories.

___ 13. Which story (or stories) involves a conflict between two different cultures that exist in the same time and place?

    A. "The Man to Send Rain Clouds"

    B. "Old Man of the Temple"

    C. both stories

    D. neither story

___ 14. What is the most important way in which the settings of "The Man to Send Rain Clouds" and "Old Man of the Temple" differ?

    A. One story takes place in the past; the other is set in the future.

    B. One story has a totally realistic setting; the other story has elements of fantasy.

    C. The two stories take place on different continents—in North America and Asia.

    D. The cultural setting is important in one story; in the other, cultural setting is unimportant.

Vocabulary

_____ 15. Which of the following might reasonably be regarded as <u>perverse</u>?
   A. deciding to walk five miles in a blinding snowstorm
   B. setting aside time to study on the evening before an important test
   C. preparing the ground before planting rose bushes
   D. wearing a helmet when you ride your bike

_____ 16. If your plans for preparing a picnic lunch went <u>awry</u>, how might you feel?
   A. overjoyed
   B. indifferent
   C. frustrated
   D. fulfilled

_____ 17. Which of the following might you fairly describe as a <u>venture</u>?
   A. saving ten dollars every week
   B. sky-diving for the first time
   C. eating dinner half an hour early
   D. trimming shrubs so that they do not become too bushy

Essay

18. In an essay, explain the importance of the cultural setting in "The Man to Send Rain Clouds" and "Old Man of the Temple." Describe what you learn about the characters and their lives from the descriptions of the cultural setting.

19. Death plays a leading role in "The Man to Send Rain Clouds" and in "Old Man of the Temple." In an essay, discuss the leading characters' attitudes toward death in these two stories. Support your main ideas with specific references to the text of each selection.

Name _____ Date _____

Narration: Short Story

Prewriting: Gathering Details

Use the following chart to list details that will help readers visualize your characters.

Questions:	Character 1:	Character 2:	Character 3:
What does each character look like?			
How does each character behave?			
What is the general attitude of each character?			
How does each character interact with others?			

Drafting: Organizing Details

Every detail in your story should increase your readers' understanding of the characters, the setting, the conflict, and the action. Use the following graphic organizer to list and organize the details of your story.

Characters	Setting	Conflict	Action

Writing Workshop—Unit 2, Part 1
Review of a Short Story: Integrating Grammar Skills

Revising Inconsistent Verb Tenses

The different forms that verbs take to show time are called tenses. When you are writing, do not change tense without a logical reason. Study the following examples.

Incorrect:	I *liked* the music but I *hate* the lyrics.
Correct:	I *liked* the music but I *hated* the lyrics.
Incorrect:	I *had walked* to school, but I *had returned* home on the bus.
Correct:	I *had walked* to school, but I *returned* home on the bus.

Use the perfect tenses to clarify a sequence of actions within the past, present, or future.

Unclear:	By the time I *finished* my homework, the TV show *ended*.
Clear:	By the time I *finished* my homework, the TV show *had ended*.
Unclear:	By tomorrow, I *walked* to school every day this week.
Clear:	By tomorrow, I *will have walked* to school every day this week.

Identifying Correct Verb Tense

A. DIRECTIONS: *Circle the verb in parentheses that best completes each sentence.*

1. By the time the train (reached, had reached) the station, over fifty people had crowded onto the platform.

2. Once the passengers (climb, climbed) on board, the conductor collects their tickets.

3. Tomorrow, I (will leave, leave) the house earlier and will take an earlier train.

Fixing Incorrect Verb Tense

B. DIRECTIONS: *On the following lines, rewrite this paragraph to correct errors in verb tense.*

Last week, my cousin Lucille and I attended a concert. Lucille purchased the tickets months before. We will walk across the park and hop on a bus to the concert hall. By the time we had arrived, the music already started. Still, we both enjoyed the concert very much.

_____

_____

_____

_____

_____

_____

_____

_____

Unit 2: Short Stories
Part 1 Benchmark Test 3

Literary Analysis: Conflict and Resolution *Read the selection. Then, answer the questions that follow.*

1. If the main character in a story struggles against the subzero cold of the Arctic, what kind of conflict is taking place?
   A. internal
   B. symbolic
   C. external
   D. generational

2. How would a character who is experiencing internal conflict feel?
   A. enthusiastic
   B. affectionate
   C. decisive
   D. confused

3. Two men glare at each other. Then, a tree falls and pins them both to the ground. What kind of conflict exists in both situations?
   A. symbolic
   B. external
   C. internal
   D. natural

4. A character is torn between his ambition to rise in society and the values that he knows to be right. What kind of conflict does such a character experience?
   A. unique
   B. symbolic
   C. external
   D. internal

Literary Analysis: Irony and Surprise Ending *Read the selection. Then, answer the questions that follow.*

Courtney ran to the door. In the week since she had last seen Michael, she had changed. When Michael, arguably the most popular boy at school, had first asked her out, Courtney had been astonished. With her wild, frizzy hair and exotic clothes, she looked nothing like the girls in Michael's social group. But now she had cut and straightened her hair and was wearing a trendy outfit borrowed from the school's fashion expert. Courtney threw open the door. Michael was so shocked that he took two steps back. Who had kidnapped the funny girl with the unusual looks—the girl he was interested in—and replaced her with this clone of a teen model?

5. What does Courtney expect to happen when Michael sees her?
   A. She expects Michael to ignore the changes in her appearance.
   B. Courtney is not sure what to expect when Michael sees the way she looks.
   C. She is worried that he might not like the changes in her appearance.
   D. Courtney believes that Michael will be delighted with her new look.

6. What happens that is unexpected?
   A. Michael is upset at Courtney's changes.
   B. Michael does not know what to think about Courtney's changes.
   C. Michael is confused about Courtney's changes.
   D. Michael is delighted with Courtney's changes.

7. Why is this selection an example of irony?
   A. It is an amusing anecdote about two teenagers.
   B. It uses symbolism to make transmit the theme.
   C. It contrasts the expected with what actually happens
   D. It describes a situation that could happen in real life.

8. Which of the following contrasts can create situational irony?
   A. a contrast between what the audience knows and what a character knows
   B. a contrast between what a character expects and what actually happens
   C. a contrast between an idea and the meaning of the words used to express it
   D. a contrast between the needs of two characters

9. Why might a surprise ending involve situational irony?
   A. The ending turns out to be different from what the characters expected.
   B. The ending has been foreshadowed from the beginning.
   C. A surprise ending uses words in a way that is not literal.
   D. A surprise ending involves a dramatic situation.

Unit 2 Resources: Short Stories
102

Literary Analysis: Setting

10. Which of the following is the best definition of the term *setting*?
    A. the story's relationship to historical events
    B. the economic conditions in an area
    C. the time and place of the action in a story
    D. the sequence of events in a story

11. Which of the following describes the setting of a selection?
    A. Juanita, a young Hispanic girl
    B. man against nature
    C. World War II Japan
    D. disillusionment

12. Which of the following settings would have a negative effect on the characters in a short story?
    A. a boat in the Atlantic Ocean
    B. an ice storm
    C. a day in winter
    D. a Saturday morning in June

13. Why is it important to pay attention to the setting of a selection?
    A. The setting may be the most interesting element in the selection.
    B. The setting provides clues to the genre of a selection.
    C. The setting contributes to character development.
    D. The setting affects characters and plot.

Reading Skill: Make Inferences

14. To make an inference, what might you apply to details in the text?
    A. the theme of the selection
    B. your prior knowledge
    C. descriptions of setting and character
    D. other people's opinions

15. What is another term that you could use in place of *inference*?
    A. educated guess
    B. thoughtless guess
    C. tentative guess
    D. random guess

Read the selection. Then, answer the questions that follow.

The supermarket was very crowded in anticipation of a holiday weekend. People were rushing in to buy charcoal for barbeques, family get-togethers, and beach parties.

16. Which question might you answer to help you make an accurate inference from the passage?
    A. What will the next holiday be?
    B. Why are people rushing around?
    C. When do people have barbeques?
    D. Why is the supermarket crowded?

17. Which details in the passage best help you make an inference about the season?
    A. barbeques, beach parties
    B. holiday weekend
    C. crowded supermarket
    D. people were rushing around

18. What can you infer about the time of year from the passage?
    A. It is winter.
    B. It is summer.
    C. It is autumn.
    D. It is spring.

19. In most cases, what is the best way to check the accuracy of an inference you make?
    A. Use common sense.
    B. Read on.
    C. Ask someone else.
    D. Use reference sources.

Reading Skill: Evaluate Visual Aids

20. What is the main purpose of signs?
    A. to warn of danger to come
    B. to regulate the flow of traffic
    C. to act as a symbol
    D. to give information quickly

21. What is the purpose of a sign that has a red circle with a diagonal line through it?
    A. to help you beware of something
    B. to let you know something is coming
    C. to tell you not to do something
    D. to warn you to look out for something

22. Which of the following is a purpose of safety signs?
    A. to show people how to do something
    B. to warn people of potential risks
    C. to tell people where to travel
    D. to provide visual reinforcement

23. Which of the following elements do all signs include?
    A. pictures
    B. text
    C. octagons
    D. information

24. How do written instructions typically differ from signs?
    A. Instructions give more details than signs.
    B. Instructions do not provide direct statements.
    C. Instructions do not give a clear message.
    D. Instructions and signs have opposite purposes.

Vocabulary: Word Roots and Prefixes

25. What is the meaning of the Latin prefix *circum-* in the words *circumference, circumscribe,* and *circumnavigate*?
    A. through
    B. between
    C. around
    D. behind

26. Using the meaning of the Latin prefix *circum-*, what is the meaning of the word *circumrotate*?
    A. to cut something out of
    B. to move away from something
    C. to repeat a continuous motion
    D. to spin around an axis as a wheel does

27. Using the meaning of the Latin root *-mot-*, what is the meaning of the word *motile*?
    A. a place to stay with parking provided for each room
    B. having the power to move spontaneously
    C. a relative on a person's mother's side of the family
    D. the tendency to show emotion readily

28. Which of the following is an antonym, or word that is the opposite meaning, for the word *introspective*?
    A. deep
    B. thoughtful
    C. insightful
    D. outgoing

Grammar: Regular and Irregular Verbs

29. What is true of all irregular verbs?
    A. They are extremely uncommon in the English language.
    B. They are linking verbs.
    C. They do not follow standard conjugation patterns.
    D. They are action verbs.

30. In what way are the following verbs similar: *have, make, come, know, and see?*
    A. They are the most common verbs in English.
    B. They are helping verbs.
    C. They are intransitive verbs.
    D. They are irregular verbs.

Grammar: Consistent Verb Tense

31. Which of the items below contains an inconsistent use of verb tense?
    A. When we arrive at the airport, Mom had already seen us.
    B. Before we left for the picnic, we packed the sandwiches.
    C. Learning to play tennis took Jean all summer, but she persevered.
    D. The music sounded playful, and we started tapping our feet.

32. Which sentence contains an error in verb tense consistency?
    A. We approached the window and bought our tickets.
    B. I see the wild geese and took a photograph.
    C. Teresa saw the film and thoroughly enjoyed it.
    D. Anyone who wishes is welcome to come to the concert.

33. Which of the following is the past participle of the word *began*?
    A. has begun
    B. begun
    C. began
    D. have begun

ESSAY

Writing

34. On a separate piece of paper, write a short adaptation of a fairy tale in which you change the setting, but retain the underlying plot. Then, create an alternate ending for the story.

35. On a separate piece of paper, write an outline of a short story that has two characters involved in a conflict with one another. Include information that explains how the conflict is resolved.

36. On a separate piece of paper, write a news story about an endangered species, including reports of suggestions for preserving the species. Remember that news stories are objective—leave out your own opinions and write in the third person.

Name _____

Unit 2: Short Stories
Part 2 Concept Map

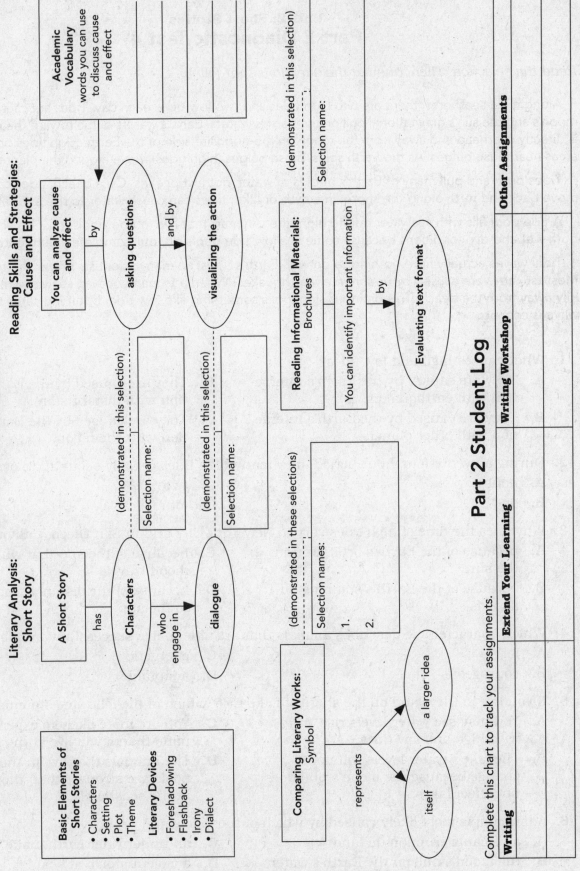

Reading Skills and Strategies:
Cause and Effect

You can analyze cause and effect

by → asking questions

and by → visualizing the action

Academic Vocabulary
words you can use to discuss cause and effect

Reading Informational Materials:
Brochures

You can identify important information

by → Evaluating text format

(demonstrated in this selection)
Selection name:

Literary Analysis:
Short Story

A Short Story

has → Characters

who engage in → dialogue

(demonstrated in this selection)
Selection name:

(demonstrated in this selection)
Selection name:

Basic Elements of Short Stories
• Characters
• Setting
• Plot
• Theme

Literary Devices
• Foreshadowing
• Flashback
• Irony
• Dialect

Comparing Literary Works:
Symbol

represents → a larger idea

→ itself

(demonstrated in these selections)
Selection names:
1.
2.

Part 2 Student Log

Complete this chart to track your assignments.

Writing	Extend Your Learning	Writing Workshop	Other Assignments

Unit 2: Short Stories
Part 2 Diagnostic Test 4

Read the selection. Then, answer the questions that follow.

Along most seashores, there are two high tides and two low tides each day. Tides are caused by the moon's and the sun's gravitational pull on the Earth's waters. Earth's waters bulge toward the moon when it is directly overhead and away from the moon on the opposite side of the Earth. High tides occur in the areas near these bulges. As the Earth spins, these bulges (high tides) move around the planet.

Tides push and pull many of Earth's bodies of water, not just oceans. On a beach, tides cause water to move back and forth along the shore. In a river or lake, tides can cause water to rise and fall.

A tide pool fills with seawater during high tide. Animals that live in tide pools must be able to live in both wet and dry conditions because some shallow tide pools dry out completely during low tides.

Tidal waves actually have nothing to do with Earth's tides, so many scientists prefer the term *tsunami*. Most tsunamis are caused by underwater earthquakes. When a tsunami occurs, seawater may rush rapidly away from the beach. This ominous sign looks something like low tide, but it indicates that a huge wave is coming.

1. What causes high and low tides?
   - A. They are caused by the Earth's interaction with earthquakes.
   - B. They are caused by the Earth's interaction with other planets.
   - C. They are caused by the Earth's interaction with distant stars.
   - D. They are caused by the Earth's interaction with the moon.

2. During a twenty-four-hour period, how many high tides usually occur at an ocean's shore?
   - A. none
   - B. one
   - C. two
   - D. four

3. Why does the time of high tides vary in New York City and in San Diego, California?
   - A. because of the Earth's orbit around the sun
   - B. because of the Earth's spinning on its axis
   - C. because of the speed at which the moon travels
   - D. because of the distance from the Earth to the sun

4. Which characteristic describes animals that are able to live successfully in tide pools?
   - A. large
   - B. courageous
   - C. energetic
   - D. adaptable

5. If you live in Cleveland on the shore of Lake Erie, which of the following statements is true?
   - A. You may see water levels rise or fall with high and low tides.
   - B. The lake's water levels will never change because the moon's pull does not affect lakes.
   - C. You are more likely to experience a tsunami than if you live at the seashore.
   - D. The animals that live in the lake's tide pools are stronger than those that live at the seashore.

6. A tsunami is most likely caused by which of the following?
   - A. a volcanic eruption on land
   - B. the moon's pull on the Earth's waters
   - C. an underwater earthquake
   - D. a violent storm at sea

7. Which of the following would make the best title for the passage?
   A. "Tides Rise, Tides Fall"
   B. "Gravitational Effects on the Moon"
   C. "Tide Pools: Not an Easy Place to Live"
   D. "History of a High Tide"

Read the selection. Then, answer the questions that follow.

The life of Dutch painter Johannes Vermeer remains a mystery. Historians identify some basic dates of significance in his life (his birth in 1632, his marriage in 1653, and his death in 1675), but most of the details of his life have been lost. His reputation, however, has been secured by a small output of about thirty-five masterpieces.

Most of Vermeer's works are genre paintings, which means they show people in everyday situations. In several paintings, a woman reads or writes a letter. In others, women play musical instruments. The locales are mostly interiors, often with a window nearby. The themes might seem commonplace, but Vermeer's presentation is extraordinary. He creates a delicate sense of light that many viewers find magical. He is also well known for his masterful placement of objects. Every detail, from a single earring to a milk jug, is carefully selected and positioned.

Close inspection of Vermeer's paintings reveals that in some paintings, he applied paint thickly to build up a heavy surface. In others, he used many layers of paints and transparent glazes, which create depth and a surprising quality of light.

Vermeer did not reject the popular style of painting in his day. Instead, he brought the style to a new height with his careful, shimmering works.

8. Which of the following correctly defines a genre painting?
   A. a painting with unusual effects of light
   B. a painting done with transparent glazes
   C. a painting of an indoor scene
   D. a painting of people in everyday life

9. Why does the writer state that Vermeer's life remains a mystery?
   A. He died mysteriously.
   B. He was a failure during his lifetime.
   C. Few details of his life are known.
   D. He produced few paintings.

10. What is Vermeer most famous for?
    A. His unusual ability to portray children.
    B. His unusual ability to portray animals.
    C. His unusual ability to portray landscapes.
    D. His unusual ability to portray light.

11. Which of the following is *not* typically found in a painting by Vermeer?
    A. portrayal of light
    B. masterful placement of objects
    C. outdoor scenery
    D. scenes of everyday life

12. Why do you suppose Vermeer included a window in so many of his paintings?
    A. Seventeenth-century Dutch houses had many decorative windows.
    B. Only rich people's homes had windows, and Vermeer's subjects were all wealthy.
    C. Windows enabled Vermeer to paint the effects of light on his subjects.
    D. Windows symbolized the human relationship with the natural world.

13. Why did Vermeer sometimes apply many layers of transparent glazes to his paintings?

    A. He liked to apply paint thickly.

    B. He could not afford to buy new paints.

    C. He used glazes to create depth and light.

    D. He used glazes to build a heavy surface.

14. Why are Vermeer's paintings described as "shimmering"?

    A. because of their sense of light

    B. because of their sense of motion

    C. because of their sense of drama

    D. because of their sense of mystery

15. Which of the following would make the best title for the passage?

    A. "The Genius of Johannes Vermeer"

    B. "The Mystery of Johannes Vermeer"

    C. "Seventeenth-Century Dutch Painters"

    D. "Dutch Genre Painters"

Vocabulary Warm-up Word Lists

Study these words from "The Necklace." Then, complete the activities.

Word List A

anguish [ANG gwish] *n.* suffering caused by pain or worry
   Imagine the anguish she felt when she heard the bad news!

distress [di STRES] *n.* great pain or sorrow
   His uncle's illness caused great distress for all family members.

estimating [ES ti may ting] *v.* judging the value or amount of something
   I am estimating that this used car is worth more than $5,000.

gracious [GRAY shuhs] *adj.* elegant; courteous; kindly considerate
   The hotel was proud of its gracious service.

homemade [HOHM MAYD] *adj.* made at home
   She served a delicious homemade cake that she had baked all by herself.

outraged [OWT rayjd] *adj.* very angry
   We felt outraged by the terrible way we were treated.

pitiful [PIT i fuhl] *adj.* provoking sorrow or sympathy
   We were embarrassed by our team's pitiful effort to win the game.

tormented [tawr MEN tid] *v.* caused physical or mental pain
   Indecision tormented her, and she tossed and turned all night.

Word List B

bargaining [BAHR guhn ing] *v.* discussing the price of something
   After bargaining for several minutes, they agreed on a fair price.

calculations [kal kyoo LAY shunz] *n.* acts of figuring out an amount or price
   According to my calculations, I'll need ten dollars more to buy the used bike.

colleagues [KAHL eegz] *n.* coworkers; associates
   She enjoyed chatting with her colleagues at the office party.

fashionable [FASH uhn uh buhl] *adj.* popular; stylish
   Everyone wanted to eat at the fashionable restaurant.

fragile [FRAJ il] *adj.* easily broken or damaged
   We were very careful not to drop the fragile vase.

funds [FUNDZ] *n.* amounts of money
   Do we have sufficient funds to pay for the trip?

grandest [GRAND est] *adj.* most impressive; very worthy
   Her grandest ambition was to be elected president.

humble [HUM buhl] *adj.* relating to a low social class; modest
   Despite his humble beginnings, he rose to a position of great authority.

111

"The Necklace" by Guy de Maupassant
Vocabulary Warm-up Exercises

Exercise A *Fill in the blanks using each word from Word List A only once.*

My brother is always complaining. Either he's angry and [1] _____ about something he read on the Internet or else he's pouting and in [2] _____ over the way his favorite football team is playing this season. If people really [3] _____ him the way he says they do, I might show him some pity. I may be guessing, but I'm [4] _____ that at least three-quarters of the [5] _____ he says he feels is his own fault. He just doesn't appreciate the [6] _____ home we live in or all the good things we have. Nothing is ever good enough for my brother. If I gave him a delicious [7] _____ cookie, he'd just complain that it's [8] _____ and not as good as the ones that come from the bakery.

Exercise B *Find a synonym for each word in Word List B. Use each synonym in a sentence that makes the meaning of the word clear. (Hint: You may use a thesaurus to look for synonyms.)*

Example: Vocabulary word: <u>bargaining</u>   synonym: *negotiating*
   We were <u>negotiating</u> with the storekeeper to get a better price.

1. <u>calculations</u>   synonym: _____
   _____

2. <u>colleagues</u>   synonym: _____
   _____

3. <u>fashionable</u>   synonym: _____
   _____

4. <u>fragile</u>   synonym: _____
   _____

5. <u>funds</u>   synonym: _____
   _____

6. <u>grandest</u>   synonym: _____
   _____

7. <u>humble</u>   synonym: _____
   _____

Name _____ Date _____

Read the following passage. Pay special attention to the underlined words. Then, read it again, and complete the activities. Use a separate sheet of paper for your written answers.

Ellie and I had been friends for a long time. Still, I felt nervous about lending her my favorite jade earrings. Wearing those earrings always made me feel as if I enjoyed a <u>gracious</u> lifestyle that I'll likely never afford.

"I won't lose them," she insisted, her pained voice dripping with <u>anguish</u>.

"I know," I said, although in the past, Ellie had proved herself less than reliable when it came to returning borrowed jewelry. I pictured her wearing my beautiful earrings with the faded <u>homemade</u> sweater that her aunt knitted for her when we were in the sixth grade. It had been a size too small for her then, and Ellie had grown another three inches. That poor old sweater was looking really <u>pitiful</u> these days.

"I bet your red blouse would look fabulous with the earrings," Ellie continued.

"My red blouse?" Visions of that lovely garment being defiled by ink spots and gravy stains enflamed my mind.

"Is that a problem?" asked Ellie, glaring at me as if to ask why I persistently <u>tormented</u> her.

"No," I whispered uneasily. I wondered if Ellie sensed my growing <u>distress</u>.

"And those sandals you're wearing . . ." she began, casting an envious glance at my feet.

"My new sandals?" I choked. The very thought of having someone else's bare feet parked in my shoes gave me a queasy feeling deep inside.

"Come on!" shouted Ellie, <u>outraged</u> by my hesitant response. "It's not as if I've ever asked for a favor before!"

I began <u>estimating</u> all the favors I had done for her over the years, and the number I came up with was higher than our ages combined. I could have argued with the girl, but what good would it do? Ellie's always been like that, and I knew she always would be.

Instead, I just smiled at my old friend and told her how terrific she'd look in my lavender silk scarf.

1. Underline the words that tell why the narrator does not expect to enjoy a <u>gracious</u> lifestyle. What is a synonym for *gracious*?

2. Circle the word that gives a clue to the meaning of <u>anguish</u>. Why is Ellie feeling *anguish*?

3. Underline the words that show that the sweater is <u>homemade</u>. What do you own that is *homemade*?

4. Circle the words that tell what was looking <u>pitiful</u>. Write a sentence about something that is *pitiful*.

5. Why would Ellie feel as if she were being <u>tormented</u>? Describe the effect that using the word *tormented* has.

6. Circle the words that hint at the narrator's growing <u>distress</u>. Write a sentence about something that might cause you to feel *distress*.

7. Circle the words that tell what Ellie is <u>outraged</u> about. Write a sentence about something that has *outraged* you.

8. Circle the word that gives a clue to the meaning of <u>estimating</u>. What does *estimating* mean?

113

"The Necklace" by Guy de Maupassant
Reading Warm-up B

Read the following passage. Pay special attention to the underlined words. Then, read it again, and complete the activities. Use a separate sheet of paper for your written answers.

Diamonds are valued all over the world for their usefulness and beauty.

Most of the diamonds mined today come from Africa, Australia, and Russia. While diamonds are fairly common in nature, gem-quality diamonds are rare and very expensive. Because they are the hardest substance in nature, more than 75 percent of all diamonds are sold for industrial purposes. The rest are used mainly in rings, necklaces, and other <u>fashionable</u> items of jewelry.

If you are thinking of buying a diamond, be sure to visit a reputable jeweler. You can choose to go to a local jeweler or one of his or her <u>colleagues</u> downtown. However, the cost of your diamond will be more or less the same in each store.

The price of diamonds depends on supply and demand, so don't expect to get a better deal by <u>bargaining</u> with the jeweler. The higher the quality, the higher the price of the diamond. <u>Calculations</u> of a diamond's quality are based on the four Cs: cut, clarity, carat weight, and color. Skilled cutters carefully shape and polish each stone to bring out its natural beauty. Although diamonds are incredibly hard, they can be very <u>fragile</u> at the same time: With a slip of the wrist, a careless cutter can easily turn a precious gem into a cracked and almost worthless chunk of stone.

Of course, the diamond itself is only one part of the jewelry you are buying. Even the <u>grandest</u> and most beautiful diamond will not look its best if it is set into an ugly ring or bracelet.

To the untrained eye, many gemstones closely resemble diamonds. Cubic zirconia, white sapphire, white topaz, and even clear glass can all be cut to look like diamonds. Anyone who lacks the <u>funds</u> to buy a real diamond might want to consider one of these less-expensive alternatives. But do not try to fool those jewelers! Their keen eyes can easily distinguish a real diamond from one of its <u>humble</u> imitators.

1. Circle two examples of <u>fashionable</u> jewelry. Write a sentence about something else that is *fashionable*.

2. Circle the word that tells what job these <u>colleagues</u> hold. Who are your *colleagues*?

3. Underline the words that tell what you might hope to get by <u>bargaining</u>. Write about a time when *bargaining* worked for you.

4. Circle the words that tell what these <u>calculations</u> are measuring. When do you do *calculations*?

5. Explain how diamonds can be hard and <u>fragile</u> at the same time.

6. Circle the words that give you a clue to the meaning of <u>grandest</u>. Write a sentence about the *grandest* thing you have seen lately.

7. What can you do if you lack the <u>funds</u> to buy a real diamond? What is a synonym for *funds*?

8. Circle the word that tells what is <u>humble</u>. In what way are they *humble*?

"The Necklace" by Guy de Maupassant
Literary Analysis: Character and Characterization

A **character** is a person, an animal, or even an object who participates in the action and experiences the events of a literary work. Writers communicate what characters are like through **characterization.** There are two main types of characterization:

- **Direct characterization:** The writer tells readers what a character is like.
- **Indirect characterization:** The writer gives readers clues to a character. The writer might show the character's behavior, present the character's words and thoughts, describe the character's physical appearance, or reveal what other characters say or think about the character. Often, when a writer uses indirect characterization, it is up to the reader to draw logical conclusions about the character's personality and motivations.

When she sat down to dinner at her round table with its three-day-old cloth, and watched her husband opposite her lift the lid of the soup tureen and exclaim, delighted: "Ah, a good homemade beef stew! There's nothing better . . ." she would visualize elegant dinners with gleaming silver amid tapestried walls peopled by knights and ladies and exotic birds in a fairy forest.

This passage gives readers a glimpse of the personalities of both Madame and Monsieur Loisel through the characters' thoughts and words.

DIRECTIONS: *On the lines provided, briefly explain how each excerpt from the story helps to characterize one or more of the characters.*

1. She suffered constantly, feeling that all the attributes of a gracious life, every luxury, should rightly have been hers. _____

   _____

   _____

2. She looked at him, irritated, and said impatiently:
   "I haven't a thing to wear. How could I go?" _____

   _____

   _____

3. "Well, all right, then. I'll give you four hundred francs. But try to get something really nice."

   _____

   _____

4. Madame Forestier said in a faintly waspish tone: "You could have brought it back a little sooner! I might have needed it." _____

   _____

   _____

5. Madame Loisel started to tremble. Should she speak to her? Yes, certainly she should. And now that she had paid everything back, why shouldn't she tell her the whole story?

   _____

   _____

"The Necklace" by Guy de Maupassant

Reading: Ask Questions to Analyze Cause and Effect

A **cause** is an event, action, or feeling that produces a result. An **effect** is the result produced. As you read, **ask questions to analyze cause and effect.** Examining these relationships helps you follow the logic that moves a story forward. As you read, ask yourself:

- What happened?
- Why did it happen?
- What happens as a result?

A single cause may produce several effects. Effects may, in turn, become causes.

A. DIRECTIONS: *Use the cause-and-effect chart below to keep track of events in "The Necklace."*

Cause	Effect
1. Monsieur Loisel receives an invitation to a reception at the Ministry.	Madame Loisel complains that she has nothing to wear.
2. _____	_____
3. _____	_____
4. _____	_____
5. _____	_____
6. _____	_____

B. DIRECTIONS: *Is the cause of the catastrophe that overtakes Madame Loisel solely of her own making? Or does the author suggest that she is, to some extent, the product of a vain and materialistic society? Discuss your response on the lines below.*

_____

_____

_____

_____

"The Necklace" by Guy de Maupassant
Vocabulary Builder

Word List

| rueful | resplendent | disheveled | profoundly |

A. DIRECTIONS: *In each item below, think about the meaning of the italicized word, and then answer the question in a complete sentence.*

1. How would a person with a *disheveled* appearance look? _____

_____

2. If you were *rueful* about one of your actions, how would you feel? _____

_____

3. Describe something that might move you *profoundly*, and tell how you would feel. _____

_____

4. Describe a *resplendent* scene that would impress you. _____

_____

B. DIRECTIONS: *For each item below, write a single sentence using the words as grouped.*

1. *resplendent* and *profoundly*

_____

2. *rueful* and *disheveled*

_____

C. DIRECTIONS: *For each numbered word, choose the word or phrase that is most nearly the same in meaning.*

___ 1. profoundly
   A. slightly   B. carefully   C. deeply   D. unpleasantly

___ 2. disheveled
   A. untidy   B. attractive   C. unimpressive   D. unusual

___ 3. resplendent
   A. dim and gloomy   C. bright and shining
   B. beautiful and memorable   D. sad and needy

___ 4. rueful
   A. forgetful   B. regretful   C. angry   D. embarrassed

"The Necklace" by Guy de Maupassant
Support for Writing an Advice Column

For your advice column addressed to Madame and Monsieur Loisel, use the lines below to jot down notes about the issues dividing them. For each issue, make a suggestion on how the characters can resolve their conflict.

Issue 1: _____

_____

My suggestions on how to resolve this issue: _____

_____

_____

_____

Issue 2: _____

_____

My suggestions on how to resolve this issue: _____

_____

_____

_____

Issue 3: _____

_____

My suggestions on how to resolve this issue: _____

_____

_____

_____

Issue 4: _____

_____

My suggestions on how to resolve this issue: _____

_____

_____

_____

Now, use your notes to write your advice column. Make a special effort not to favor one character over the other. Keep your tone neutral, and revise any language that sounds biased in favor of one of the characters.

"The Necklace" by Guy de Maupassant

Support for Extend Your Learning

Listening and Speaking

Use the lines below to take notes for what Madame Loisel will tell her husband about the true value of the lost necklace.

How Madame Loisel feels after she learns the truth about the necklace: _____

_____

_____

What she is thinking: _____

_____

_____

Whether she will be defensive or apologetic or both: _____

_____

_____

What gestures she might use: _____

_____

_____

Research and Technology

Use the chart below to make notes for your informative brochure about diamonds. Keep track of your sources.

Physical Facts About Diamonds	How Diamonds Are Mined
_____	_____
_____	_____
_____	_____
Uses of Diamonds	**Why Diamonds Are Valuable**
_____	_____
_____	_____
_____	_____

Name _____ Date _____

"The Necklace" by Guy de Maupassant
Enrichment: Defining Values

Human values are beliefs people hold about which behaviors, jobs, activities, possessions, and ideas are truly important or valuable in life. You can usually tell what people value by observing how they spend their time, what they say, and how they treat others.

In "The Necklace," differing values are demonstrated by Madame and Monsieur Loisel. Readers can observe Madame Loisel's captivation with society and material possessions. She spends her time wishing to live a life like that of her wealthy friend, Madame Forestier. Her husband, on the other hand, is content with their humble life.

DIRECTIONS: *Answer the following questions regarding the values of characters in* "The Necklace."

1. What are the values of Madame Loisel and Madame Forestier? Explain.

   _____

   _____

   _____

   _____

2. What does Monsieur Loisel seem to value? In what ways are his values different from those of his wife? Explain.

   _____

   _____

   _____

   _____

3. Do you think Madame Loisel's values might change after her enduring ten years of hard work? If so, in what ways might her values change?

   _____

   _____

   _____

   _____

"The Necklace" by Guy de Maupassant
Selection Test A

Critical Reading *Identify the letter of the choice that best answers the question.*

____ 1. Which city is the setting for "The Necklace"?
   A. London
   B. Paris
   C. Rome
   D. New York

____ 2. At the beginning of the story, what is the cause of Madame Loisel's constant unhappiness?
   A. her marriage
   B. her desire to be wealthy
   C. her poor health
   D. her wish for more friends

____ 3. What literary technique is illustrated by this passage from Maupassant's story?
   She would have so loved to charm, to be envied, to be admired and sought after.
   A. irony
   B. symbolism
   C. direct characterization
   D. indirect characterization

____ 4. What conclusion might you draw about Madame Loisel's character, based on the life she wants to live?
   A. She enjoys working.
   B. She has simple needs.
   C. She cares most about her relationships.
   D. She cares most about material things.

____ 5. What conclusion can you draw about Monsieur Loisel, based on his treatment of his wife?
   A. He cares a lot about his wife's happiness.
   B. He has grown tired of his wife's complaints.
   C. He cares too much about unimportant things.
   D. He enjoys accompanying his wife to fancy receptions.

___ 6. Which word best describes Madame Loisel's friendship with Madame Forestier?
A. equality
B. companionship
C. sympathy
D. envy

___ 7. Where does Madame Loisel lose Madame Forestier's necklace?
A. at Madame Forestier's house
B. during a visit to the library
C. on a trip
D. at the ball

___ 8. Which of the following is a direct effect of Madame Loisel's loss of the necklace?
A. a bitter quarrel with Madame Forestier
B. divorce from Monsieur Loisel
C. the couple's move from the city to the countryside
D. a life of poverty and hard physical labor

___ 9. Choose the order in which these events happen in Maupassant's story.
   I.   Madame Loisel borrows the necklace.
   II. Madame Loisel meets Madame Forestier on the Champs Elysées.
   III. Monsieur Loisel receives an invitation for a reception at the Ministry.
   IV. Madame Loisel writes her friend a letter to explain the delay in returning the necklace.
A. IV, I, III, II
B. III, I, IV, II
C. III, II, I, IV
D. II, IV, I, III

___ 10. Which of the following literary elements is prominent in the story's ending?
A. metaphor
B. irony
C. flashback
D. point of view

___ 11. Which of the following best states the theme, or underlying message, of "The Necklace"?
A. It is dangerous to attach too much importance to wealth.
B. It is foolish to try to escape one's fate.
C. People should not get too deeply into debt.
D. It is foolish to give in to a spouse's demands.

_____ 12. Which word best describes Madame Loisel's feelings at the end of the story?

    A. happiness

    B. indifference

    C. astonishment

    D. fear

Vocabulary and Grammar

_____ 13. Which word most nearly means the same as *rueful* as it is used in this sentence?

    The very sight of the little Breton girl who cleaned for her awoke rueful thoughts and the wildest dreams in her mind.

    A. cheerful

    B. angry

    C. sorrowful

    D. pleasant

_____ 14. Which sentence uses the word *disheveled* correctly?

    A. At the ball, Madame Loisel looks *disheveled* in her fine gown and necklace.

    B. Monsieur Loisel brings home a *disheveled* invitation to a grand reception.

    C. Years of hard labor had resulted in Madame Loisel's *disheveled* appearance.

    D. Madame Loisel yearns for a *disheveled* life, complete with elegant furnishings.

_____ 15. Which kind of verb connects the subject to a word that renames or describes the subject? This sentence from "The Necklace" contains one.

    Madame Loisel <u>was</u> a great success.

    A. an action verb

    B. a transitive verb

    C. an irregular verb

    D. a linking verb

Essay

16. In "The Necklace," the necklace represents many aspects of Madame Loisel's character. The necklace also relates to the story's theme, or underlying message about human life and behavior. In an essay, discuss the significance of the necklace. Be sure to include your own statement of the story's theme.

17. In an essay, analyze the relationship between Madame Loisel and her husband. As you plan your writing, consider the following questions: How does Madame Loisel treat her husband? What does her treatment of him say about her personality and her priorities in life? How does Monsieur Loisel treat his wife? What can you conclude about his values, based on his relationship with her?

"The Necklace" by Guy de Maupassant
Selection Test B

Critical Reading *Identify the letter of the choice that best completes the statement or answers the question.*

____ 1. At the beginning of "The Necklace," what is the main cause of Madame Loisel's constant unhappiness?
A. her turbulent marriage
B. her desperate longing to be wealthy
C. her weakness and failing health
D. her loneliness and isolation

____ 2. What literary technique is used in the following passage from "The Necklace"?
Instead of being delighted, as her husband had hoped, she tossed the invitation on the table and muttered, annoyed: "What do you expect me to do with that?"
A. irony
B. flashback
C. direct characterization
D. indirect characterization

____ 3. From her thoughts, speeches, and behavior, we can conclude that Madame Loisel admires a society that values, above all,
A. a work ethic.
B. money and possessions.
C. family and friends.
D. creativity and the arts.

____ 4. Based on the life that Madame Loisel craves, what can you conclude about her character?
A. She wants to help those less fortunate.
B. She cares most about her relationships.
C. She is realistic and sincere.
D. She is self-centered and materialistic.

____ 5. What can you conclude about the personality of Madame Loisel's husband, based on his treatment of her?
A. He is patient and tolerant, and he cares a great deal about his wife's happiness.
B. He is impatient and has grown tired of listening to his wife's complaints.
C. He is petty and cares too much about trifles.
D. He is pleasure-loving and enjoys accompanying his wife to fancy receptions.

____ 6. Which quotation best reveals Monsieur Loisel's attitude toward his wife?
A. "What's the matter? You've really been very strange these last few days."
B. "Wait—you silly thing!"
C. "I'll give you four hundred francs. But try to get something really nice."
D. "You must write to your friend," he said, "and tell her that you've broken the clasp of the necklace and that you're getting it mended."

____ 7. Why does Madame Loisel feel "anguish" when she asks to borrow the necklace?
   A. She is humiliated at having to borrow the necklace.
   B. She dreads going to the reception.
   C. She lacks confidence in her beauty.
   D. Madame Forestier gives her too many pieces to choose from.

____ 8. What best characterizes Madame Loisel's friendship with Madame Forestier?
   A. They are old school friends who lead very similar lives.
   B. They enjoy each other's company and spend a lot of time shopping together.
   C. Madame Loisel pities Madame Forestier for the shallow life she leads.
   D. Madame Loisel envies Madame Forestier and finds it difficult to visit her.

____ 9. What is an effect that results from Madame Loisel's loss of the necklace?
   A. Monsieur Loisel loses his job with the Ministry of Education.
   B. Madame Loisel leaves her husband and returns to her parents.
   C. The Loisels move from the city to the countryside.
   D. Her husband gives up all his inheritance from his father.

____ 10. What does this passage suggest about Madame Loisel?

   Madame Loisel came to know the awful life of the poverty-stricken. However, she resigned herself to it with unexpected fortitude. The crushing debt had to be paid. She would pay it.

   A. She remains consistently selfish and self-centered.
   B. She is capable of great strength of character.
   C. She is terrified by the enormity of their debt.
   D. She is grateful to her husband and regrets the way she has treated him in the past.

____ 11. What is most likely the author's purpose in this passage from "The Necklace"?

   But sometimes, when her husband was at the office, she would sit down by the window and muse over that party long ago when she had been so beautiful, the belle of the ball.

   A. to show that Madame Loisel only lives in the past
   B. to reveal how Madame Loisel's life has coarsened her emotions
   C. to inject a note of sympathy for Madame Loisel
   D. to show that, after all these years, Madame Loisel still resents her husband

____ 12. Madame Forestier reveals that the diamond necklace she had lent Madame Loisel was fake. What literary element is Maupassant using in this surprise ending?
   A. metaphor
   B. irony
   C. foreshadowing
   D. personification

____ 13. The theme, or underlying message, of "The Necklace" concerns the danger of
   A. attaching excessive importance to wealth.
   B. trying to evade one's fate or destiny.
   C. borrowing money from a friend.
   D. working excessive long hours.

Vocabulary and Grammar

____ 14. Which word is most nearly the opposite of *rueful* as it is used in this sentence?

The very sight of the little Breton girl who cleaned for her awoke rueful thoughts and the wildest dreams in her mind.

    A. mournful
    B. agitated
    C. cheerful
    D. remorseful

____ 15. Which sentence uses the word *resplendent* correctly?

    A. As she dances, Madame Loisel looks *resplendent* in her gown and necklace.
    B. In a *resplendent* tone, Madame Forestier reproaches her friend for being so late.
    C. For the Loisels, the loss of the necklace is a *resplendent* catastrophe.
    D. Monsieur Loisel cherishes the *resplendent* hope of their finding the necklace.

____ 16. Which term correctly identifies the verb *was* in this sentence from "The Necklace"?

It was Madame Forestier, still young, still beautiful, still charming.

    A. action verb
    B. transitive verb
    C. irregular verb
    D. linking verb

____ 17. Which item correctly identifies the italicized verb in the following sentence?

After choosing the diamond necklace, Madame Loisel *fled* with her treasure.

    A. linking verb
    B. transitive action verb
    C. intransitive action verb
    D. past participle

____ 18. Which sentence contains a linking verb?

    A. Monsieur Loisel seems truly horrified by the loss of the necklace.
    B. The couple searches everywhere for the missing necklace.
    C. Monsieur Loisel borrows thousands of francs.
    D. Madame Loisel wears down her pink nails on the bottoms of saucepans.

Essay

19. In an essay, explain the significance of the necklace in Guy de Maupassant's story. How does the necklace symbolize Madame Loisel's character and her life? What might the necklace symbolize in Madame Loisel's society or cultural context? How does the necklace relate to the theme of the story?

20. In an essay, analyze the relationship between Madame Loisel and her husband by answering the following questions: How does Madame Loisel treat her husband? What does her treatment of him say about her priorities? How does her husband treat her? What can you conclude about his values, based on his relationship with her?

Vocabulary Warm-up Word Lists

Study these words from "Rules of the Game." Then, complete the activities.

Word List A

chess [CHES] *n.* board game for two players
The game of <u>chess</u> ended when she trapped her opponent's king.

concealed [kuhn SEELD] *adj.* hidden
I spent hours searching for the <u>concealed</u> message in the document.

deliberately [di LIB uhr uht lee] *adv.* on purpose
Did you do that <u>deliberately</u>, or was it an accident?

essential [i SEN shuhl] *adj.* important and necessary
Knowing how to spell is <u>essential</u> to solving crossword puzzles.

proclaimed [proh KLAYMD] *v.* officially announced
Israel <u>proclaimed</u> its independence in 1948.

relented [ri LENT id] *v.* gave up; yielded; weakened
She finally <u>relented</u> and let me borrow the car.

triumphant [try UM fuhnt] *adj.* successful; victorious
When we won the hard-fought game, we felt <u>triumphant</u>.

trophy [TROH fee] *n.* prize for winning a competition
I keep the <u>trophy</u> I won on a shelf in my room.

Word List B

encased [en KAYSD] *v.* covered or surrounded completely
The glass <u>encased</u> the delicate sculpture so that no one would touch it.

menu [MEN yoo] *n.* list of food items available in a restaurant
We chose our desserts from the last page of the <u>menu</u>.

obscured [uhb SKYOORD] *v.* prevented from being seen or heard
The clouds <u>obscured</u> the moon from view.

protective [pruh TEK tiv] *adj.* shielding; safeguarding
The dentist applied a <u>protective</u> coating to his teeth to prevent decay.

pungent [PUN juhnt] *adj.* having a strong smell or taste
The <u>pungent</u> aroma of garlic filled the pizza shop.

regional [REE juh nuhl] *adj.* relating to a particular area or region
Kimchi is a <u>regional</u> dish that is popular in Korea.

reveal [ri VEEL] *v.* make known; show; display
After you guess, I will <u>reveal</u> the correct answer.

specialized [SPE shuh lyzd] *v.* focused on a particular activity
Dr. Seuss <u>specialized</u> in writing children's books.

"Rules of the Game" by Amy Tan
Vocabulary Warm-up Exercises

Exercise A *Fill in the blanks using each word from Word List A only once.*

My favorite game is checkers. To become good at any game, it is [1] _____
to practice every day. When I am [2] _____ in a tournament, I am proud to
bring home a [3] _____ as a symbol of my victory. It may be true that
checkers is a simpler game than [4] _____, but the strategies that a good
player must learn can be very complex. In one tournament, I [5] _____
pretended to be confused about the rules. I [6] _____ my knowledge
of the game so that my opponent would underestimate my ability. As soon as he
made a mistake, I pounced! When I jumped four of his checkers in one move, he finally
[7] _____, and I was [8] _____ the winner. Victory is sweet!

Exercise B *Answer the questions with complete explanations.*

1. Why would your mother have <u>encased</u> her wedding china?
   _____

2. What kinds of items would you expect to find on a breakfast <u>menu</u>?
   _____

3. What would you do if you were riding a bicycle and something <u>obscured</u> your view
   of the road?
   _____

4. How would you probably respond to a <u>pungent</u> aroma?
   _____

5. What kinds of things might a <u>protective</u> mother do?
   _____

6. Whom would your neighbors be likely to call if they needed help with a <u>regional</u>
   problem?
   _____

7. If a library were <u>specialized</u>, what sort of things might you expect to find there?
   _____

8. If you want someone's advice, should you <u>reveal</u> your true feelings? Why or why not?
   _____

Name _____ Date _____

Read the following passage. Pay special attention to the underlined words. Then, read it again, and complete the activities. Use a separate sheet of paper for your written answers.

No one knows for sure when the game of <u>chess</u> was invented. An early version of the game was popular by the end of the tenth century. The modern game was developed in southern Europe a few centuries later.

Players in the sixteenth century wanted others to study their games and become better players. The best players were <u>proclaimed</u> "masters" and were highly honored. Chess masters who were at first reluctant to tell their secrets soon <u>relented</u>. At last, they allowed their games to be recorded. Instruction books were <u>essential</u> to the growing popularity of the game. Books on chess were soon being read all over the world.

Paul Morphy was the first great American chess player. He defeated all his American rivals at an early age before traveling to Europe in 1858. There, he was <u>triumphant</u> over the greatest players of his time. The onset of mental illness brought an abrupt end to Morphy's brilliant career.

After the Russian Revolution, the Russian government <u>deliberately</u> set out to dominate world chess. It set up a program of chess education for children. It offered financial support to the country's best players. Russian players dominated the game throughout the twentieth century. Russian dominance was briefly interrupted when the American chess master Bobby Fischer took home the world championship <u>trophy</u> in 1972.

Computer programs that play chess first appeared in the 1960s, but these programs were no match for the top human players. It was not until 1997 that a chess computer called Deep Blue was able to narrowly defeat world champion Garry Kasparov in a series of games. Kasparov <u>concealed</u> his disappointment as best he could, but he could not hide the embarrassment he felt over losing to a machine.

Today, computers make it easier for chess players at all levels of skill to practice and improve their games.

1. Circle the word that tells what <u>chess</u> is. What board games do you enjoy?

2. Circle the words that tell who were <u>proclaimed</u> "masters" and how they were rewarded. Then, tell what *proclaimed* means.

3. Underline the words that tell what the masters were reluctant to do before they <u>relented</u>. Why do you think they *relented*?

4. Underline the words that tell what made instruction books <u>essential</u>. Why do you think they were *essential*?

5. Circle the name of the player who was <u>triumphant</u>. Write about something at which you have been, or would like to be, *triumphant*.

6. Circle the words that tell what the Russian government <u>deliberately</u> set out to do. Describe something you have done *deliberately*.

7. Circle the words that tell what kind of <u>trophy</u> Bobby Fischer won. How do you think the Russians felt about losing the *trophy*?

8. Circle the word that tells what <u>concealed</u> means. How do you think Kasparov *concealed* his disappointment?

Name _____   Date _____

"Rules of the Game" by Amy Tan
Reading Warm-up B

Read the following passage. Pay special attention to the underlined words. Then, read it again, and complete the activities. Use a separate sheet of paper for your written answers.

San Francisco's Chinatown is the second-largest Chinese community in the United States. Rebuilt after the 1906 earthquake, it became a major tourist attraction in the 1920s. Today, tourists from all over flock to Chinatown to visit the many fascinating shops and superb restaurants that line the crowded streets.

Begin your tour at the Chinatown Gate. Stroll along Grant Avenue and peek into some of the unique shops you pass along the way. You will find that the shop windows have <u>encased</u> unusual objects of every description. Some shops sell everything from valuable antiques to inexpensive trinkets. Others concentrate on one specific kind of item. The Clarion Music Center, for example, has long <u>specialized</u> in selling traditional musical instruments from China and Tibet, while the TenRen Tea Shop offers more than fifty kinds of <u>regional</u> teas imported from different areas of China. Of course, you do not have to enter every shop to find out what is inside. A quick peek at the window display will usually <u>reveal</u> the kinds of things being offered for sale.

With so many tempting restaurants to choose from, deciding where to have lunch can be a problem. Be sure to look at the <u>menu</u> displayed outside each restaurant before making your choice. After lunch, stroll past the Buddhist temples on Waverly Place. Enjoy the <u>pungent</u> smell of incense that wafts out onto the street. You might even see the Golden Gate Bridge if the city's famous thick fog has not completely <u>obscured</u> it.

The most interesting part of a visit to Chinatown, of course, is the people who live there. Be sure to visit the teeming fruit and vegetable stands on Stockton Street. There, many local people do their daily grocery shopping. In Portsmouth Square, you will see elderly grandparents keeping a close watch over the children who run around on the busy playground. Like mothers and fathers everywhere, the parents and grandparents of Chinatown are fiercely <u>protective</u> of their children!

1. Circle the words that tell what the shop windows <u>encased</u>. Write a sentence using the word *encased*.

2. Underline the sentence that gives a clue to the meaning of <u>specialized</u>. Describe a store that has *specialized* in something you like.

3. Underline the words that tell where the <u>regional</u> teas come from. What *regional* products come from your part of the country?

4. Underline the words that tell what a quick peek will <u>reveal</u>. Explain what *reveal* means.

5. Why is it a good idea to look at the <u>menu</u> before choosing a restaurant?

6. Circle the words that tell what is <u>pungent</u>. What other things might be described as *pungent*?

7. Why might the bridge be <u>obscured</u>? Explain what *obscured* means.

8. Underline the words that tell you who is <u>protective</u>. Of whom or what are you *protective*?

"Rules of the Game" by Amy Tan
Literary Analysis: Character and Characterization

A **character** is a person, an animal, or even an object who participates in the action and experiences the events of a literary work. Writers communicate what characters are like through **characterization.** There are two main types of characterization:

- **Direct characterization:** The writer tells readers what a character is like.
- **Indirect characterization:** The writer gives readers clues to a character. The writer might show the character's behavior, present the character's words and thoughts, describe the character's physical appearance, or reveal what other characters say or think about the character. Often when a writer uses indirect characterization, it is up to the reader to draw logical conclusions about the character's personality and motivations.

The next week I bit back my tongue as we entered the store with the forbidden candies. When my mother finished her shopping, she quietly plucked a small bag of plums from the rack and put it on the counter with the rest of the items.

In this example, we get a glimpse of the characters' personalities through their actions. Meimei's mother rewards her for learning the secret of invisible strength and biting back her tongue.

DIRECTIONS: *On the lines provided, briefly explain how each excerpt from the story helps to characterize one or more of the characters.*

1. My mother imparted her daily truths so she could help my older brothers and me rise above our circumstances.

   _____

   _____

2. When we got home, my mother told Vincent to throw the chess set away. "She not want it. We not want it," she said, tossing her head stiffly to the side with a tight, proud smile.

   _____

   _____

3. At the next tournament, I won again, but it was my mother who wore the triumphant grin. "Lost eight piece this time. Last time was eleven. What I tell you? Better off less!" I was annoyed, but I couldn't say anything.

   _____

   _____

4. My mother would proudly walk with me, visiting many shops, buying very little. "This my daughter Wave-ly Jong," she said to whoever looked her way.

   _____

   _____

"Rules of the Game" by Amy Tan

Reading: Ask Questions to Analyze Cause and Effect

A **cause** is an event, action, or feeling that produces a result. An **effect** is the result produced. As you read, **ask questions to analyze cause and effect.** Examining these relationships helps you follow the logic that moves a story forward. As you read, ask yourself the following questions:

- What happened?
- Why did it happen?
- What happens as a result?

A single cause may produce several effects. For example, a character who is saving to buy a bicycle takes a baby-sitting job with her neighbor's children. This leads to her starting a summer play group and starts her thinking about getting a college degree in early childhood education.

Effects may, in turn, become causes. That same character's successful experiences with young children leads her to volunteer on the pediatric floor of a local hospital.

DIRECTIONS: *Use the cause-and-effect chart below to keep track of events in "Rules of the Game."*

Cause	Effect
1. The Jong family goes to a church Christmas party.	Vincent gets a secondhand chess set.
2. Vincent and Winston play chess a lot.	_____ _____
3. _____	_____ _____
4. _____	_____ _____
5. _____	_____ _____
6. _____	_____ _____
7. _____	_____ _____

Name _____ Date _____

"Rules of the Game" by Amy Tan
Vocabulary Builder

Word List

| pungent | benevolently | retort | malodorous |

A. DIRECTIONS: *In each item below, think about the meaning of the italicized word, and then answer the question in a complete sentence.*

1. If a dish tastes *pungent,* is it spicy or bland? _____

   _____

2. If you reply to a person with a *retort,* are you speaking sweetly or sharply? _____

   _____

3. You enter a restaurant and notice that the air is *malodorous.* Explain why you would choose to eat there or not. _____

   _____

4. If a classmate looks at you *benevolently,* do you feel happy or frightened? _____

   _____

B. DIRECTIONS: *For each item below, write a single sentence using the words as grouped.*

1. *pungent* and *retort*

   _____

   _____

2. *benevolently* and *malodorous*

   _____

   _____

C. DIRECTIONS: *For each numbered word, choose the word or phrase that is most nearly the same in meaning and write its corresponding letter on the line.*

____ 1. pungent
   A. painful   B. unpleasant   C. sharp-smelling   D. sweet-tasting

____ 2. benevolently
   A. kindly   B. offensively   C. critically   D. maliciously

____ 3. retort
   A. joke   B. reply   C. move   D. surprise

____ 4. malodorous
   A. spiteful   B. ugly   C. filthy   D. stinking

"Rules of the Game" by Amy Tan
Support for Writing an Advice Column

For your advice column addressed to Waverly and her mother, use the lines below to jot down notes about the issues dividing Waverly and her mother, Mrs. Jong. For each issue, make a suggestion on how the characters can resolve their conflict.

Issue 1: _____

_____

My suggestions on how to resolve this issue: _____

_____

_____

_____

Issue 2: _____

_____

My suggestions on how to resolve this issue: _____

_____

_____

_____

Issue 3: _____

_____

My suggestions on how to resolve this issue: _____

_____

_____

_____

Issue 4: _____

_____

My suggestions on how to resolve this issue: _____

_____

_____

_____

Now, use your notes to write your advice column. Make a special effort not to favor one character over the other. Keep your tone neutral, and revise any language that sounds biased in favor of one of the characters.

"**Rules of the Game**" by Amy Tan
Support for Extend Your Learning

Listening and Speaking
Use the lines below to take notes for Waverly's monologue about chess.

Waverly's Feelings and Thoughts About Chess

_____
_____
_____
_____

Waverly's Relationship With Her Mother

_____
_____
_____
_____

Research and Technology
Use the lines below to make notes for your informative brochure about how to play chess.

1. Description of chess board and pieces _____
_____

2. How each piece moves _____
_____
_____

3. How play begins _____
_____

4. How the game ends _____
_____

5. What is a draw? _____
_____

"Rules of the Game" by Amy Tan
Enrichment: Performing Arts

Waverly discovers something that she is good at only after her brother happens to receive a chess set as a Christmas present. She pursues her interest in the game without any urging from her mother or her brothers. Consider the steps Waverly takes first to learn the game and then to improve her skills.

- Waverly reads the instruction book.
- She reads other books from the library about chess.
- She plays with her brothers.
- She learns to visualize the entire game in her head.
- She practices by herself by imagining chess moves and games on a drawn chessboard next to her bed.
- She plays against more experienced opponents.

Waverly devotes a great deal of time and energy to her new-found talent. Her talent, commitment, and self-discipline are the keys to her success as a chess champion.

Commitment and self-discipline are the keys to success as a performing artist as well. Whether they are actresses, pianists, or dancers, performing artists work very hard to acquire their skills and to improve them.

DIRECTIONS: *Think of a performing art that interests you. It might be ballroom dancing or ballet, singing, acting, or playing an instrument. Then answer these questions.*

Performing art in which I am interested: _____

1. What steps do you think you would have to take to acquire skill and then to improve your skill in this performing art? List the steps here.

   a. _____   f. _____

   b. _____   g. _____

   c. _____   h. _____

   d. _____   i. _____

   e. _____   j. _____

2. How do your steps for *acquiring* your skill compare with the steps Waverly took to learn chess? _____

   _____

   _____

3. How do your steps for *improving* your skill compare with the steps Waverly took to improve her game? _____

   _____

   _____

4. What role would commitment and self-discipline play if you were to pursue and be successful at your chosen performing art? _____

   _____

Name _____ Date _____

"Rules of the Game" by Amy Tan
"The Necklace" by Guy de Maupassant
Build Language Skills: Vocabulary

Word Roots

The Latin root -ver- comes from *verus*, the Latin word for "truth." English words that contain this root, such as *verify* and *verdict*, have meanings related to "truth" and "true."

Not all words with the letters *v-e-r* indicate the Latin root -ver-. English words with the letters *v-e-r* may be related to the root -verd-, meaning "green," or to the root -vert-, meaning "turn."

A. DIRECTIONS: *Look up the origin of each of the following words. Write its root (-ver-, -verd-, or -vert-) on the line. Then, write a sentence using the word in a context that makes its meaning clear.*

1. verify _____

_____

2. verisimilitude _____

_____

3. subversion _____

_____

4. verdant _____

_____

5. vertical _____

_____

Academic Vocabulary Practice

B. DIRECTIONS: *Answer each question using the italicized Academic Vocabulary word.*

1. How does a flashback affect the *sequence* of events in a story? _____

_____

2. Does the title of an essay often identify the writer's *topic*? _____

_____

3. What are some words you might use to describe a writer's tone—his or her *attitude* toward the subject or the characters in a work? _____

_____

4. How can you *verify* the cause-and-effect relationship of events in a story? _____

_____

5. What does the use of quotation marks around a sentence *imply* about the sentence?

_____

Name _____ Date _____

"Rules of the Game" by Amy Tan
"The Necklace" by Guy de Maupassant
Build Language Skills: Grammar

Action and Linking Verbs, Transitive and Intransitive Verbs

A. DIRECTIONS: *Write the answers to each of the following questions in the lines provided.*

1. What is an *action verb*? _____

_____

2. Write an original sentence using an action verb. _____

_____

3. What is a *linking verb*? _____

_____

4. Write an original sentence using a linking verb. _____

_____

5. On the lines below, explain the difference between a *transitive verb* and an *intransitive verb*. Then, give an example of each.

_____

_____

_____

_____

B. DIRECTIONS: *Read each of the following sentences, noting the verb in italics. Then, circle the letter of the item that correctly identifies each verb.*

1. Meimei *appeared* especially happy after winning the tournament.
   A. action verb   B. linking verb
2. Meimei *pondered* her next move.
   A. transitive verb   B. intransitive verb
3. Madame Loisel *danced* at the party until nearly 4 A.M.
   A. action verb   B. linking verb
4. Monsieur Loisel *paled* at the news.
   A. transitive verb   B. intransitive verb

"Rules of the Game" by Amy Tan
Selection Test A

Critical Reading *Identify the letter of the choice that best answers the question.*

____ 1. What do Meimei and her brothers think about the section of Chinatown where they live?
   A. They think it is dull and boring.
   B. They are afraid of it.
   C. They hate the poverty they see there.
   D. They think it is a place of adventure.

____ 2. At the beginning of the story, what causes Mrs. Jong to buy a small bag of plums for Meimei?
   A. Meimei has completed her weekly chores.
   B. Meimei has learned the art of invisible strength from her mother.
   C. Meimei has asked her mother to buy the plums.
   D. Mrs. Jong wants to reward Meimei for winning a chess tournament.

____ 3. When the family returns home after the Christmas party, Mrs. Jong tells Vincent to throw away the chess set. What does this remark show about Mrs. Jong's character?
   A. She does not like playing chess.
   B. She thinks Vincent will be wasting his time with the chess set.
   C. She is proud and does not want to keep a second-hand gift.
   D. She has a sly sense of humor.

____ 4. Why does Meimei's mother believe it is important for Meimei to figure out the rules of chess for herself?
   A. to beat her brothers at the game
   B. to respect her Chinese heritage
   C. to compete successfully in America
   D. to become a national chess champion

____ 5. Why does Meimei tell her mother that she doesn't want to play in the local tournament because "they would have American rules"?
   A. She does not understand the American rules for playing chess.
   B. She is afraid of losing in the tournament.
   C. She uses a strategy so that her mother will let her play in the tournament.
   D. She uses a strategy to avoid traveling far from home.

_____ 6. Why does Meimei say that shopping with her mother is a duty she cannot avoid?
  A. She would rather be playing with her brothers.
  B. She hates the crowded markets.
  C. She is embarrassed by her mother's behavior.
  D. She has to skip a chess tournament.

_____ 7. How does Meimei feel about her mother's involvement in her chess success?
  A. happy
  B. proud
  C. puzzled
  D. annoyed

_____ 8. An author may give clues to a character's personality by reporting what other characters say or think about the character. What is this technique called?
  A. foreshadowing
  B. symbolism
  C. direct characterization
  D. indirect characterization

_____ 9. Choose the order in which these events happen in the story.
  I.   Meimei learns about opening moves in a chess game.
  II. Vincent receives a chess set.
  III. Meimei's brothers lose their interest in chess.
  IV. Meimei uses her Life Savers to replace the missing chess pieces.
  A. I, III, II, IV
  B. I, IV, II, III
  C. II, IV, I, III
  D. III, I, IV, II

_____ 10. What is a special privilege Meimei gets at home so that she can practice chess?
  A. Mrs. Jong teaches Meimei the art of invisible strength.
  B. Mrs. Jong agrees not to throw the instruction book away.
  C. Meimei has the bedroom to herself because her brothers sleep in the living room.
  D. Meimei is allowed to go home from the market by herself.

_____ 11. What other game, besides chess, does the story's title refer to?
  A. the conflict between Vincent and Winston
  B. a strategy for achieving success in life
  C. a plan to become a national chess champion
  D. the conflict between Meimei's parents

Vocabulary and Grammar

___ 12. Which phrase explains the meaning of *pungent*?

A. producing a sharp smell

B. tasteless and bland

C. creamy and filling

D. well-cooked and crispy

___ 13. Which sentence uses the word *benevolently* correctly?

A. Lau Po smiles *benevolently* at Meimei and agrees to play chess with her.

B. Meimei yells *benevolently* at the man who has just insulted her.

C. Mrs. Jong reacts *benevolently* when Meimei runs away from the market.

D. The secret to success at chess is to treat your opponent *benevolently*.

___ 14. Which sentence contains a linking verb?

A. Meimei is calm.

B. Meimei learns the rules quickly.

C. Meimei runs through the alleyways.

D. Meimei wins many tournaments.

___ 15. Which sentence contains an intransitive verb?

A. Meimei mastered the endgame in chess.

B. Mrs. Jong often attended the tournaments.

C. Vincent eventually lost interest in chess.

D. Meimei ran swiftly through the alleys.

Essay

16. When Mrs. Jong looks at the chess instruction booklet, she says:

"This American rules," she concluded at last. "Every time people come out from foreign country, must know rules. You not know, judge say, Too bad, go back. They not telling you why so you can use their way go forward. They say, Don't know why, you find out yourself. But they knowing all the time. Better you take it, find out why yourself."

In a brief essay, explain what Mrs. Jong is trying to teach Meimei about immigrant life in America. Use details from the story to support your view.

17. In an essay, describe the personalities of the two main characters in the story, Meimei and Mrs. Jong. How are they similar to, and different from, each other? Considering their personalities, do you think the conflict between them is likely to continue? Why or why not?

"Rules of the Game" by Amy Tan
Selection Test B

Critical Reading *Identify the letter of the choice that best completes the statement or answers the question.*

____ 1. What causes Mrs. Jong to buy Meimei a small bag of plums?
    A. She is rewarding Meimei for completing her weekly chores without being reminded.
    B. She is rewarding Meimei for practicing the art of invisible strength.
    C. She buys the plums because Meimei asks for them.
    D. She buys the plums because Meimei has just won a chess tournament.

____ 2. How do Meimei and her brothers view the Chinatown alley where they live?
    A. as a dull and spiritless place
    B. as a terrifying and dangerous place
    C. as a poverty-stricken environment
    D. as a place of great adventure

____ 3. What do the following lines reveal about Mrs. Jong's character?

    When we got home, my mother told Vincent to throw the chess set away. "She not want it. We not want it," she said, tossing her head stiffly to the side with a tight, proud smile.

    A. She is stubborn and does not like the game of chess.
    B. She is hard-working and thinks Vincent will be wasting his time if he learns to play chess.
    C. She is proud and does not want to keep a gift that is obviously second-hand.
    D. She is determined and has a sly sense of humor.

____ 4. Why does Mrs. Jong say that Meimei should figure out the rules of chess for herself?
    A. She wants Meimei to prove that girls can play chess just as well as boys.
    B. She wants Meimei to retain all that is valuable in her Chinese heritage.
    C. She wants Meimei to be able to compete successfully in America.
    D. She wants Meimei to become a national chess champion.

____ 5. Meimei says that the power of chess is that "it is a game of secrets in which one must show and never tell." What does this way of looking at the game suggest about Meimei's character?
    A. She recognizes this strategy as helpful in dealing with other situations in life.
    B. She has very little competitive spirit.
    C. She is ambitious to become the youngest grandmaster.
    D. She will always repress her true feelings about living in Chinatown.

____ 6. Why does Meimei tell her mother that she does not want to play in the local tournament because "they would have American rules"?
    A. She feels she does not know enough yet to compete in a tournament.
    B. She is afraid of losing in the tournament and being embarrassed.
    C. She is saying the opposite of what she wants so that her mother will let her play.
    D. She does not want to play in tournaments in her home town.

____ 7. Why does Meimei view shopping with her mother as "the one duty I couldn't avoid"?
A. She would rather be outside playing with her friends.
B. She dislikes the crowded markets and shopping in general.
C. She hates the fact that her mother shows her off.
D. She regrets having to skip all Saturday chess tournaments.

____ 8. Meimei finds Mrs. Jong's behavior in the shops very embarrassing. How does her reaction indirectly characterize Meimei?
A. Meimei is vain and upset when people don't recognize her.
B. Meimei is sensitive and resents being paraded around to make her mother look good.
C. Meimei is friendly and enjoys the attention she gets from strangers.
D. Meimei is selfish and resents the time spent away from playing or studying chess.

____ 9. How does Meimei feel about her mother's involvement in her chess success?
A. She thinks her mother's behavior is very amusing.
B. She is proud that her mother takes such an interest in her.
C. She is sympathetic because she knows her mother never was able to play chess.
D. She is annoyed and wishes her mother would let her alone to practice.

____ 10. Which statement represents the main cause of conflict between Meimei and Mrs. Jong?
A. Meimei wears her hair in pigtails; Mrs. Jong keeps hers short.
B. Meimei knows how to play chess; Mrs. Jong does not.
C. Meimei has become famous; Mrs. Jong is jealous of her success.
D. Meimei understands and wants to live by "American rules"; Mrs. Jong does not.

____ 11. For Mrs. Jong, what is the real significance of Meimei's success?
A. Mrs. Jong is instrumental in helping her daughter learn the chess rules.
B. Meimei achieves success within the American system that her mother cannot.
C. Meimei is offered a scholarship to college.
D. Meimei's success enhances the family's status in their village in China.

____ 12. Choose the order in which these events happen in "Rules of the Game."
I. Meimei plays chess with Lau Po in the park.
II. Vincent and Winston play chess and will not let Meimei play.
III. Meimei runs away from her mother and stays away for two hours.
IV. Meimei wins her first chess tournament.
A. II, III, IV, I
B. I, II, III, IV
C. II, I, IV, III
D. II, I, III, IV

____ 13. Which of the following is an example of a concession made by Meimei's family so that she can practice chess?
A. Mrs. Jong teaches Meimei the art of invisible strength.
B. Mrs. Jong agrees to learn to play chess so she can play with Meimei.
C. Mrs. Jong gives Meimei sole use of the bedroom.
D. Mrs. Jong allows Meimei to stay home from the market on Saturdays.

____ 14. The title, "Rules of the Game," refers to chess as well as
   A. the conflict between Meimei and her two brothers.
   B. a strategy for achieving success in America.
   C. a strategy for becoming a national chess champion.
   D. the conflict between Meimei's parents and their children.

Vocabulary and Grammar

____ 15. Which sentence uses the word *retort* correctly?
   A. Meimei typically opens her chess games with a *retort*.
   B. Meimei could not think of a *retort* that would satisfy her mother.
   C. Mrs. Jong likes to deliver a *retort* to the other parents at the tournaments.
   D. A *retort* is an excellent accompaniment for steamed dumplings.

____ 16. Which phrase best defines *benevolently* as it is used in this sentence?

   "Little sister, been a long time since I play with dolls," he said, smiling benevolently.

   A. in a clumsy way
   B. in a reluctant way
   C. in a well-meaning way
   D. in a nimble or agile way

____ 17. Which sentence contains a linking verb?
   A. Meimei is a national chess champion by her ninth birthday.
   B. Meimei loses only eight pieces during the next game.
   C. Mrs. Jong studies the book of chess instructions.
   D. Meimei challenges Lau Po to a game of chess.

____ 18. Which of the following best defines a transitive verb?
   A. a verb that expresses a state of being
   B. a verb that connects the subject to a word that renames or describes the subject
   C. a verb that directs action toward someone or something named in the same sentence
   D. a verb that does not direct action toward a noun

____ 19. Which sentence contains an action verb that is intransitive?
   A. Meimei detours through the playground at the end of her alley.
   B. Mrs. Jong is extremely proud of her daughter.
   C. Meimei still needs hundreds of points for the title of grandmaster.
   D. Mrs. Jong quietly lays the bag of plums on the counter.

Essay

20. The setting of a story is the time and place in which the story takes place. Setting contributes to the atmosphere or mood of the story and helps give the characters and events their own special "flavor." In an essay, describe the significance of the setting of "Rules of the Game." Support your statements with specific examples from the story.

21. In an essay, analyze the tone of "Rules of the Game." Is the story dominated by stressful emotions and a serious theme, or does Amy Tan use touches of humor to lighten or moderate the tone? Support your ideas about the story's tone with specific examples from the text.

Study these words from "Blues Ain't No Mockin Bird." Then, complete the activities.

Word List A

breeding [BREED ing] *n.* upbringing, manners, and social skills
   The young girl's polite manner showed good <u>breeding</u>.

grove [GROHV] *n.* group of trees standing together
   We stopped at the house by the lemon <u>grove</u> to buy some fruit.

grumpy [GRUHM pee] *adj.* easily annoyed and tending to complain
   I am always <u>grumpy</u> and out of sorts when I do not get enough sleep.

ladle [LAY duhl] *n.* deep spoon with a long handle
   My grandmother has a special <u>ladle</u> for dishing up soup.

mental [MEN tuhl] *adj.* relating to or happening in the mind
   Thinking is a <u>mental</u> activity that requires exercising the mind.

mortal [MAWR tuhl] *adj.* causing death; extreme; intense
   We were in <u>mortal</u> danger when that grizzly bear crossed our path.

original [uh RIJ uh nuhl] *adj.* completely new and different
   The artist's ideas are <u>original</u>; she sees things in a way that others do not.

spooky [SPOO kee] *adj.* strange or frightening
   The clouds over the moon added to the <u>spooky</u> feeling of the night.

Word List B

amongst [uh MUNGST] *prep.* in the middle of
   We kept the secret <u>amongst</u> ourselves and did not tell anyone else.

campaign [kam PAYN] *n.* series of actions to achieve a specific result
   Our club is starting a <u>campaign</u> to encourage teens not to smoke.

consider [kuhn SID er] *v.* think about
   You should <u>consider</u> taking a bottle of water with you on the hike.

film [FILM] *n.* material used to take photos or record moving pictures
   I lost my vacation photos when the camera and <u>film</u> fell overboard.

misery [MIZ uh ree] *n.* great suffering or unhappiness
   He was in <u>misery</u> from the worst toothache ever.

reckless [REK luhs] *adj.* not careful
   It was a <u>reckless</u> decision to hike alone when a storm was coming.

speckled [SPEK uhld] *adj.* covered with many small spots or marks
   The <u>speckled</u> dog looked like it was splattered with brown paint.

underfoot [uhn der FOOT] *adv.* under the feet or on the ground
   The ice stung <u>underfoot</u> and made the cat eager to go back inside.

"Blues Ain't No Mockin Bird" by Toni Cade Bambara
Vocabulary Warm-up Exercises

Exercise A *Fill in the blanks using each word from Word List A only once.*

Have you ever been alone and heard a [1] _____ sound? It puts me in

[2] _____ dread that someone is after me. I always grab something for

protection, such as a [3] _____ from the kitchen. I could break a window

with the long handle and escape, if needed. I think that is an [4] _____

idea that no one else would have and shows that fear sharpens my

[5] _____ skills. The whole experience can also make me feel

[6] _____ and annoyed. Once I was afraid, and then I learned that the

sound I feared was coming from the neighbor's walnut [7] _____, where

branches were brushing against a ladder. I wanted to yell at whoever had left the ladder

there, but I remembered my [8] _____ and just sighed with relief!

Exercise B *Circle* T *if the statement is true or* F *if the statement is false. Then, explain your answer.*

1. If you <u>consider</u> ordering a pizza, you do not even think about it.
   T / F _____

2. If you were <u>amongst</u> friends, you would probably feel uncomfortable.
   T / F _____

3. A <u>campaign</u> to boost school spirit may include holding rallies for sports teams.
   T / F _____

4. If leaves are crunching <u>underfoot</u>, you are enjoying a walk on a fall day.
   T / F _____

5. If you fell and rolled in the mud, your clothes might be <u>speckled</u> with it.
   T / F _____

6. Someone in <u>misery</u> is usually easy to cheer up.
   T / F _____

7. Doing something <u>reckless</u> shows others that you are responsible.
   T / F _____

8. <u>Film</u> is to a traditional camera as gasoline is to a traditional car.
   T / F _____

"Blues Ain't No Mockin Bird" by Toni Cade Bambara

Reading Warm-up A

Read the following passage. Pay special attention to the underlined words. Then, read it again, and complete the activities. Use a separate sheet of paper for your written answers.

Matilda put her powder-blue suitcase into the car as her older brother Ned told her to hurry. She understood he was <u>grumpy</u> because he was tired from packing. She crawled into the car and wished she could sleep, but her mind was too full of thoughts and <u>mental</u> images of how this day might end.

Matilda groaned when Ned pressed his face onto the window with his nose pushed up, as if his manners and <u>breeding</u> had developed in a barnyard. She was glad he was in a better mood, yet how could he joke right now? They were about to live with someone they did not know. Matilda was in <u>mortal</u> fear that she would be miserable. She knew her reaction was extreme, but she could not help it. Her father was gone, looking for work; their house was rented to another family. Matilda climbed out of the car and grabbed a last apple from the tree in the yard. It was odd to think that strangers would eat her apples and downright <u>spooky</u> to think that her powder-blue room was not hers anymore.

It was a long drive and nearly dark when they arrived. Matilda was cheered to see an apple <u>grove</u> beside the house. At least there would be trees with apples to pick when she was hungry, just like at home. The woman who greeted them was older than Matilda expected and her heart sank—but only until she began to know her.

Aunt Winifred might have an old-fashioned name, but she was full of new and <u>original</u> ideas. She was a celebrated cook with her own line of natural foods; in fact, she welcomed them holding a <u>ladle</u>. She was creating a recipe for organic applesauce and spooned out several bowls, asking their opinions.

Matilda had never thought much about applesauce, but something told her she would be thinking about a lot of new things with Aunt Winifred. After all, an old lady with powder-blue streaks in her hair—yes, real racing stripes—was sure to be full of surprises!

1. Underline what Ned did that shows he was <u>grumpy</u>. Circle what the passage says made him *grumpy*.

2. Circle words that are clues to the meaning of <u>mental</u>. What is a *mental* image?

3. Circle the word that is a clue to <u>breeding</u>. Underline what Ned did that made Matilda question his *breeding*.

4. Circle the word that is a clue to <u>mortal</u>. Explain what being in *mortal* fear would be like.

5. Circle the word that is a clue to <u>spooky</u>. Describe something you think is *spooky*.

6. Circle the word that is a clue to <u>grove</u>. What would a *grove* look like?

7. Circle the clue to <u>original</u>. If you have an *original* idea, what does that mean?

8. Circle the words that describe what you do with a <u>ladle</u>. What kinds of foods are served with a *ladle*?

"Blues Ain't No Mockin Bird" by Toni Cade Bambara
Reading Warm-up B

Read the following passage. Pay special attention to the underlined words. Then, read it again, and complete the activities. Use a separate sheet of paper for your written answers.

The 1930s were a desperate time for America. The country was in the grip of the Great Depression. A famous photo from that era symbolizes the <u>misery</u> of millions who lost their jobs and often their homes and were driven to hopelessness. It is called "Migrant Mother," and it was taken by a young photographer named Dorothea Lange. Her camera, and the <u>film</u> on which her images were captured, provided a moving record for history.

Lange was a portrait photographer from San Francisco. She was hired in 1934 by the California government for a <u>campaign</u> to document the living conditions of migrant laborers. This was not an ordinary series of efforts by a state government to check on workers who moved about picking crops. These were families, mainly from the lower Midwest, who were flocking to California to escape the "dust bowl." A drought in places like Oklahoma had left the land bone dry. Then, ferocious windstorms turned farms into deserts. <u>Reckless</u> farming methods were also to blame. The land had been irresponsibly overworked to produce as much as possible. Many did not <u>consider</u> the possibility that the soil might get worn out.

It was in this situation that Lange began her work. She photographed in overcrowded migrant camps <u>amongst</u> those who set up shelter where they could. Lange's detailed reports on work and camp conditions raised the attention of the federal government, which hired her to continue documenting the problems of countless people during the Depression.

It was a woman in a lean-to tent, with children huddled <u>underfoot</u>, who inspired Lange's most memorable photo. In it, the mother's face is lined with worry. The children, <u>speckled</u> with dirt, cling to her. Lange wrote: "She had just sold the tires of her car to buy food. . . . [She] seemed to know that my pictures might help her. . . ." Indeed, Lange's photographs prompted federal and state agencies to provide aid and hope for the many in need.

1. Underline the phrase that explains what caused <u>misery</u> during the Great Depression. Give an antonym for *misery*.

2. Circle the device that uses <u>film</u>. Underline words that explain what the *film* was used for.

3. Underline the phrase that explains the purpose of the <u>campaign</u>. Circle the phrase that gives a clue to the meaning of *campaign*.

4. Circle the word that is a clue to <u>reckless</u>. If you thought a friend was being *reckless*, what would you do?

5. What did many of the farmers fail to <u>consider</u>? What was the result?

6. Explain where Lange was photographing when she was *amongst* the migrants.

7. Circle the word that tells who was <u>underfoot</u>. Explain what you think *underfoot* means in this sentence.

8. Describe what the children who were <u>speckled</u> with dirt would look like in the photo.

"Blues Ain't No Mockin Bird" by Toni Cade Bambara
Literary Analysis: Dialogue and Dialect

Dialogue is a conversation between or among characters in a literary work. In prose, dialogue is usually set off by quotation marks, and a new paragraph indicates a change in speaker. Writers use dialogue to

- reveal character traits and relationships.
- advance the action of the plot and to develop the conflict.
- add variety, color, and realism to narratives.

To make characters even more vivid and to help establish a story's setting, authors may write dialogue that reflects characters' dialect. **Dialect** is a way of speaking that is common to people of a particular region or group. A dialect's words, pronunciations, and grammar are different from those used in the standard form of a language. In the dialect of the American South, for example, speakers often do not pronounce the *g* at the ends of *-ing* words. Dialect often makes characters' personalities, as well as the setting of a story, more vivid.

A. DIRECTIONS: *On the lines provided, briefly explain what each passage of dialogue from the story reveals about the speakers.*

1. "Now, aunty," Camera said, pointin' the thing straight at her.
   "Your mama and I are not related."

   _____

   _____

2. "So here comes . . . this person . . . with a camera, takin pictures of the man and the minister and the woman. Takin' pictures of the man in his misery about to jump, cause life so bad and people been messin' with him so bad. This person takin' up the whole roll of film practically. But savin a few, of course."

   _____

   _____

3. "You standin in the misses' flower bed," say Granddaddy. "This is our own place."

   _____

B. DIRECTIONS: *On the lines below, rewrite each of the passages in dialect in standard English.*

1. Granny wasn't sayin nuthin.

   _____

2. Me and Cathy were waitin, too, cause Granny always got something to say.

   _____

3. And Granny just stare at the twins till their faces swallow up the eager and they don't even care any more about the man jumpin.

   _____

   _____

"Blues Ain't No Mockin Bird" by Toni Cade Bambara
Reading: Visualize the Action to Analyze Cause and Effect

A **cause** is an event, action, or feeling that produces a result. An **effect** is the result produced. When reading a story, **visualize the action to analyze cause and effect.** Examining these relationships helps you follow the logic that drives the plot of a story.

- Based on details in the text, picture the setting, the characters, and the action.
- Use the details of your mental picture to help you identify the relationships between actions and events.

DIRECTIONS: *Use the lines provided to answer the following questions about cause-and-effect relationships in "Blues Ain't No Mockin Bird."*

1. **A.** Why does Granny tell the children a story about a photographer taking pictures of a man about to jump from a bridge?

   _____

   _____

   B. What is the effect of this story?

   _____

   _____

2. **A.** Why does the male hawk suddenly appear in the story?

   _____

   _____

   B. What effect does the hawk have on Smilin and Camera?

   _____

   _____

   C. How does Granddaddy Cain react to the hawk's appearance?

   _____

   _____

3. **A.** Why does Granddaddy Cain smash the reporters' camera?

   _____

   _____

   B. What effect does this action have on the reporters?

   _____

   _____

Name _____ Date _____

"Blues Ain't No Mockin Bird" by Toni Cade Bambara
Vocabulary Builder

Word List

reckless   formality

A. DIRECTIONS: *In each item below, think about the meaning of the italicized word, and then answer the question.*

1. If your older brother's driving is *reckless*, would you be nervous about riding in a car with him? Explain.

   _____

   _____

2. If someone treats you with *formality*, would your overall impression be of politeness or rudeness? Explain.

   _____

   _____

B. DIRECTIONS: *Write an original sentence using each of the words below.*

1. *reckless*

   _____

   _____

2. *formality*

   _____

   _____

C. DIRECTIONS: *For each numbered word, choose the word or phrase that is most nearly the same in meaning.*

____ 1. formality
   A. lack of form   C. attention to customs
   B. deep respect   D. rudeness

____ 2. reckless
   A. nervous   C. selfish
   B. careless   D. cautious

"Blues Ain't No Mockin Bird" by Toni Cade Bambara
Support for Writing an Informal Letter

For your informal letter from the point of view of a character in the story other than the narrator, use the lines below to jot down notes under each heading.

Character Writing the Letter: _____

Personality Traits of This Character	Events and Details the Character Observed
_____	_____
_____	_____
_____	_____
_____	_____
_____	_____
_____	_____
_____	_____
_____	_____
_____	_____
_____	_____
_____	_____
_____	_____
_____	_____
_____	_____
_____	_____
_____	_____
_____	_____
_____	_____

Now, use your notes to write your informal letter to a friend or relative. Be sure that the details you include and the language you use are consistent with the personality traits you have listed for your character.

Name _____ Date _____

"Blues Ain't No Mockin Bird" by Toni Cade Bambara
Support for Extend Your Learning

Listening and Speaking

Together with a partner, use the lines below to jot down notes for what each character says in the dialogue. You may want to start by having the cameraman report what happened at Granny's house.

What the Cameraman Says	What the Boss Says in Reply
_____	_____
_____	_____
_____	_____
_____	_____
_____	_____
_____	_____
_____	_____
_____	_____
_____	_____

Research and Technology

Use the chart below to make notes for your photo collection about birds of prey.

Species	Diet	Picture Resources
_____	_____	_____
_____	_____	_____
_____	_____	_____
_____	_____	_____
_____	_____	_____
_____	_____	_____
_____	_____	_____
_____	_____	_____
_____	_____	_____
_____	_____	_____
_____	_____	_____
_____	_____	_____

Name _____ Date _____

"Blues Ain't No Mockin Bird" by Toni Cade Bambara
Enrichment: Journalism

In "Blues Ain't No Mockin Bird," the two men, "Smilin" and "Camera," are "filming for the county," whatever that means. They do not identify themselves or explain why they want to film Granny's home and family.

Assuming that the two men are journalists, or news reporters, they do not perform very admirably. They film people in the yard without asking permission, and they do not leave when it is clear that they are not welcome.

Responsible journalists conduct themselves according to a code of ethics that guides how they acquire information, what kind of information they acquire, and how they report it. Certain sources of information are acceptable, such as personal interviews, news conferences, or news wire services. When it comes to personal interviews, responsible journalists request a meeting, prepare thoroughly, and take notes or get permission to tape the interview. Then they report on the interview in a way that accurately represents the words, attitudes, and beliefs of the subject. Compare this method with how "Smilin" and "Camera" approach the narrator's family.

A. DIRECTIONS: *Interview a journalism teacher or a journalist who works for a local newspaper office or television station. Find out whether your subject or your subject's employer has a written code of ethics for journalists to follow in acquiring and reporting information. Obtain a copy if possible. Find out how your subject has applied the code of ethics in his or her own job, and try to obtain specific examples of choices that your subject has made based on ethics.*

Use the space on this page to begin to prepare for your interview. Jot down at least six specific questions you will ask. Remember to be ready to follow up these questions with other questions based on your subject's answers. Send a letter of thanks to your subject following the interview.

1. _____
2. _____
3. _____
4. _____
5. _____
6. _____

B. DIRECTIONS: *Now, summarize the results of your interview. Prepare a presentation in which you state in your own words a general code of ethics for journalists to follow. Use facts, details, and anecdotes from your interview to support your statement.*

Name _____ Date _____

Selection Test A

Critical Reading *Identify the letter of the choice that best answers the question.*

____ 1. What is the main conflict at the beginning of "Blues Ain't No Mockin Bird"?
  A. Granny vs. the men with the camera
  B. Cathy vs. the twins
  C. the narrator vs. Bingo, the dog
  D. Granny vs. Granddaddy

____ 2. Which of the following best defines *dialect?*
  A. the conversation between or among the characters in a story
  B. the comparison of two unlike objects
  C. the speech common to people of a particular region or group
  D. the analysis of cause and effect in the plot of a story

____ 3. When you visualize the setting of this passage from "Blues Ain't No Mockin Bird," what conclusion can you make?

  "Nice things here," said the man, buzzin his camera over the yard. The pecan barrels, the sled, me and Cathy, the flowers, the printed stones along the driveway, the trees, the twins, the toolshed.

  A. The story takes place in a crowded city.
  B. The story takes place in a rural area.
  C. The story takes place in a tropical country.
  D. The story takes place on the edge of a desert.

____ 4. In "Blues Ain't No Mockin Bird," Granny addresses her husband as "Mister Cain." Which of the following is the best explanation for this habit?
  A. It shows that Granny feels superior to her husband.
  B. It is a sign of emotional distance between husband and wife.
  C. It shows that Granny pities her husband.
  D. It is a sign that Granny respects her husband.

____ 5. In "Blues Ain't No Mocking Bird," Toni Cade Bambara describes "the cameraman duckin and bendin and runnin and fallin, jigglin the camera and scared." What tone does she convey through this description?
  A. anger
  B. ridicule
  C. pity
  D. disinterest

____ 6. When you visualize the action in this passage from "Blues Ain't No Mockin Bird," what effect do you think Granny's silent stare has on the twins?

> "Yeh, did he jump?" say Terry all eager. And Granny just stared at the twins till their faces swallow up eager and they don't even care any more about the man jumpin.

    A. It makes them angry.
    B. It makes them ashamed.
    C. It makes them even more curious.
    D. It puzzles them.

____ 7. In "Blues Ain't No Mockin Bird," why does the giant hawk come "flyin into things reckless with crazy"?
    A. The hawk is attacking a chicken.
    B. The hawk is attacking the camera man.
    C. The hawk is trying to claim its mate.
    D. The hawk is returning to its nest.

____ 8. In "Blues Ain't No Mockin Bird," which detail is most responsible for Granddaddy's appearance of great power and strength?
    A. his feet
    B. his hands
    C. his height
    D. his cool manner

____ 9. When you visualize the action in this passage from "Blues Ain't No Mockin Bird," what inference can you make?

> Granddaddy Cain straight up and silent, watchin the circles of the hawk, then aimin the hammer off his wrist. The giant bird fallin, silent and slow.

    A. The hawk is frightened and suddenly flies away.
    B. Granddaddy kills the hawk when he throws the hammer.
    C. Granddaddy throws the hammer but misses the hawk.
    D. The hawk suddenly attacks Granddaddy.

____ 10. In "Blues Ain't No Mockin Bird," the man nicknamed Camera calls Granny "aunty." Granny tells him, "Your mama and I are not related." What does this passage of dialogue reveal about Granny's character?
    A. She is friendly and easy-going.
    B. She can be sharp-tongued and ironic.
    C. She doesn't understand Camera's project.
    D. She welcomes strangers and makes them feel at home.

_____ 11. Which of the following best expresses the basic subject dealt with in "Blues Ain't No Mockin Bird"?

A. an old man's violent anger toward a pair of hawks

B. an old woman's strict manner with her grandchildren

C. an old woman's fury at not being treated with respect

D. a family's rudeness to a pair of reporters

Vocabulary and Grammar

_____ 12. Which word is most nearly the opposite of *reckless*?

A. cautious   C. silly

B. rash   D. hopeful

_____ 13. Which is the best definition of *formality* as it is used in this sentence?

Like his mama, Miss Myrtle, tell us never mind the formality as if we had no better breeding than to call her Myrtle, plain.

A. usual accuracy   C. necessary generosity

B. established rules   D. customary neatness

_____ 14. In a sentence, which group of words tells whom or what the sentence is about?

A. appositive phrase   C. subject

B. introductory clause   D. predicate

_____ 15. Which item correctly identifies the underlined part of this sentence?

Cathy <u>pulled up her socks and giggled.</u>

A. subject   C. direct object

B. predicate   D. prepositional phrase

Essay

16. In an essay, describe the character of Granny in "Blues Ain't No Mockin Bird." Include examples of her words and actions, and explain what they reveal about her.

17. In "Blues Ain't No Mockin Bird," Toni Cade Bambara often uses dialogue for the characters. She also uses dialect in both the narrative and the dialogue. In an essay, explain how these two techniques affect your emotional response to the story.

"Blues Ain't No Mockin Bird" by Toni Cade Bambara
Selection Test B

Critical Reading *Identify the letter of the choice that best completes the statement or answers the question.*

____ 1. Early in "Blues Ain't No Mockin Bird," what conflict does the author establish?
  A. Granny vs. the moving picture men
  B. Cathy vs. Tyrone
  C. the children vs. Bingo
  D. Granny vs. Granddaddy

____ 2. When you visualize the setting in this passage from "Blues Ain't No Mockin Bird," you can infer that the action takes place

  "Nice things here," said the man, buzzin his camera over the yard. The pecan barrels, the sled, me and Cathy, the flowers, the printed stones along the driveway, the trees, the twins, the toolshed.

  A. in a crowded city in the Northwest.
  B. in a rural area.
  C. in a densely populated suburb.
  D. in a valley between two mountains.

____ 3. When the man nicknamed Camera addresses Granny as "aunty," Granny says to him, "Your mama and I are not related." What does this bit of dialogue reveal about Granny?
  A. She is friendly and easy-going.
  B. She can be sharp-tempered and ironic.
  C. She doesn't understand Camera's project.
  D. She dislikes all visitors.

____ 4. Which of the following items best defines *dialect*?
  A. the conversation between or among characters in a literary work
  B. the attribution of human qualities to nonhuman objects
  C. a way of speaking that is common to people of a particular region or group
  D. a hypothesis about cause and effect

____ 5. In "Blues Ain't No Mockin Bird," how does the detail "about this lady Goldilocks who barged into a house that wasn't even hers" help a reader to understand Cathy's character?
  A. It shows that she likes to make the twins laugh.
  B. It points out how she keeps the twins from bothering Granny.
  C. It reveals her interest in storytelling.
  D. It illustrates that she likes to follow Granny's example.

____ 6. Granny's habit of addressing her husband as "Mister Cain" is a sign of
  A. superiority.
  B. distance.
  C. dislike.
  D. respect.

____ 7. When you visualize the action in this passage from "Blues Ain't No Mockin Bird," what effect do you think Granny's silent stare has on the twins?

> "Yeh, did he jump?" say Terry all eager. And Granny just stared at the twins till their faces swallow up eager and they don't even care any more about the man jumpin.

A. It makes them furious at Granny.
B. It makes them feel ashamed for asking.
C. It makes them even more curious.
D. It confuses and baffles them.

____ 8. Why does the giant hawk come "wailin up over the meadow, flyin low and tilted and screamin, zigzaggin through the pecan grove . . . flyin into things reckless with crazy"?
A. The hawk has lost its bearing while pursuing a chicken.
B. The hawk is distracted by a glint of sunshine from the camera man's camera.
C. The hawk is furiously eager to claim its mate.
D. The hawk is upset that Granddaddy has destroyed its nest.

____ 9. When Toni Cade Bambara describes the cameraman "duckin and bendin and runnin and fallin, jigglin the camera and scared," what tone, or attitude toward her subject, is she conveying?
A. anger
B. ridicule
C. pity
D. disinterest

____ 10. In "Blues Ain't No Mockin' Bird," what aspect of Granddaddy's appearance is most responsible for the impression he gives of great power and strength?
A. his huge hands
B. his large feet
C. his great height
D. his cool manner

____ 11. Use the details in this passage from "Blues Ain't No Mockin Bird" to visualize the scene. What can you infer was the result of Smilin's and Granddaddy's actions?

> And Smilin jumpin up and down swipin at the huge bird, tryin to bring the hawk down with just his raggedy ole cap. Granddaddy Cain straight up and silent, watchin the circles of the hawk, then aimin the hammer off his wrist. The giant bird fallin, silent and slow.

A. Smilin chases the bird away before Granddaddy throws his hammer.
B. Smilin's actions are ineffectual, but Granddaddy kills the hawk with his hammer throw.
C. Smilin waves his cap after Granddaddy misses the hawk with his hammer throw.
D. Smilin's actions infuriate the hawk, which then attacks Granddaddy.

____ 12. How does Granny and Granddaddy's relationship parallel that of the two hawks?
A. They prefer each other's company to that of outsiders.
B. They have lived in one place all their lives.
C. They are deeply attuned to the abundance of nature.
D. They are fiercely loyal to each other.

____ 13. The theme, or central message, of "Blues Ain't No Mockin Bird" has to do with
   A. an old man's violent anger toward a pair of hawks.
   B. an old woman's strict manner with her grandchildren.
   C. an old woman's fury at not being treated with respect.
   D. a family's rudeness to a pair of reporters.

Vocabulary and Grammar

____ 14. Which phrase is the best synonym for *formality*?
   A. reverence for tradition
   B. attention to established rules and customs
   C. openminded willingness to listen to others
   D. meticulous attention to detail

____ 15. Which of the following is typical of the dialect of the American South?
   A. Speakers rarely use the past tense of verbs.
   B. Speakers confuse subject and object pronouns.
   C. Speakers use very short sentences.
   D. Speakers often do not pronounce the *g* at the ends of *-ing* words.

____ 16. Which phrase best defines the subject of a sentence?
   A. a word or group of words that tells whom or what the sentence is about
   B. a group of words that contains at least one adjective
   C. a word that stands at the very beginning of a sentence
   D. a word that expresses physical or mental action

____ 17. What is the underlined part of this sentence? Cathy <u>pulled up her socks.</u>
   A. an appositive phrase.
   B. the predicate.
   C. the indirect object.
   D. a prepositional phrase.

____ 18. The complete predicate consists of
   A. the complete subject and the verb.
   B. the simple subject and the simple predicate.
   C. the verb and the direct object.
   D. the verb and all the words associated with it.

Essay

19. In "Blues Ain't No Mockin Bird," dialogue and dialect are important literary devices. In an essay, explain how dialogue helps to reveal character traits and relationships, as well as to move the story forward. Also explain how use of dialect adds variety, color, and realism.

20. Granddaddy Cain is a powerful figure in "Blues Ain't No Mockin Bird." Readers are introduced to this character as he calms down his wife and loads up the truck, "madder than Granny in the first place." When readers finally meet Granddaddy Cain, he is described as "so tall and quiet and like a king." Then readers see how he deals with the hawk and the two reporters. In an essay, explain what you learn about Granddaddy Cain from each of these incidents, and how each incident prepares you for the next.

Study these words from "The Invalid's Story." Then, complete the activities.

Word List A

ambition [am BISH uhn] *n.* strong desire to succeed
   She has the <u>ambition</u> to be class president and will work hard.

cheerless [CHEER lis] *adj.* gloomy; dreary; dismal
   The room was dark, dirty, and <u>cheerless</u>, with only a chair to sit on.

considerable [kuhn SID uh ruh buhl] *adj.* large; substantial; sizable
   Stop now because it is a <u>considerable</u> distance to the next gas station.

distressed [di STREST] *adj.* worried or upset
   I was <u>distressed</u> by the news that our team had lost the finals.

drenched [DRENCHT] *v.* made completely wet; covered completely
   We did not have an umbrella and got <u>drenched</u> by the rain.

impressed [im PREST] *v.* influenced favorably; overwhelmed
   He <u>impressed</u> me with his knowledge of other cultures.

railway [RAYL way] *adj.* having to do with a railroad
   The most popular <u>railway</u> car is always the one with the snack bar.

stifling [STYF ling] *adj.* extremely hot
   Without a fan or a window to open, the room was <u>stifling</u>.

Word List B

consultation [kuhn suhl TAY shuhn] *n.* discussion to reach an agreement
   We held a <u>consultation</u> with the family doctor to decide how to best treat Grandma's illness.

detect [di TEKT] *v.* to notice or discover
   I <u>detect</u> a problem because they will not answer my questions.

overdue [oh ver DOO] *adj.* not on time; late
   My report is <u>overdue</u> because I can't find the time to finish it.

pathetic [puh THET ik] *adj.* causing pity or sorrow
   With his ragged clothes and tired face, the old man looked <u>pathetic</u>.

placidly [PLAS id lee] *adv.* in a calm and peaceful way
   We were <u>placidly</u> minding our own business when we heard a scream.

remembrance [ri MEM bruhns] *n.* memory of a person, thing, or event
   Flags are often placed on soldiers' graves as a sign of <u>remembrance</u>.

sufferings [SUHF er ings] *n.* physical or mental pains or sorrow
   Added to their injuries, the lack of food and supplies made their <u>sufferings</u> greater.

unendurable [uhn en DOOR uh buhl] *adj.* too terrible to be tolerated
   The crowded plane and small seats made the long flight <u>unendurable</u>.

Unit 2 Resources: Short Stories
161

"The Invalid's Story" by Mark Twain
Vocabulary Warm-up Exercises

Exercise A *Fill in the blanks using each word from Word List A only once.*

When it was time to head for the [1] _____ station, no one had any

[2] _____ to leave. Everyone was tired. Traveling requires

[3] _____ energy. No matter how [4] _____ you are by

the wonders of a place, after a while you just want to rest. On top of all that, we were

[5] _____ by the weather outside. There was a downpour and we were

sure to get [6] _____ on our walk to the station. When we got outside,

the air in the tropical heat was so [7] _____ that getting soaked was

actually a relief. All in all, we were a [8] _____ group when we got on the

train. Then, our traveling spirit returned. We were off to our next destination!

Exercise B *Circle T if the statement is true or F if the statement is false. Then, explain your answer.*

1. If you are waiting <u>placidly</u>, you are in a hurry to get started.
   T / F _____

2. You might be worried about a friend who was meeting you and is long <u>overdue</u>.
   T / F _____

3. A player with a lot of skill would make a <u>pathetic</u> team member.
   T / F _____

4. Two groups that were cooperating on a project would never hold a <u>consultation</u>.
   T / F _____

5. War and poverty are two causes of people's <u>sufferings</u> in the world.
   T / F _____

6. An animal with good hearing would not <u>detect</u> a low sound.
   T / F _____

7. A problem that is <u>unendurable</u> probably has an easy solution.
   T / F _____

8. A <u>remembrance</u> of a dead relative is usually a reason for cheerful celebration.
   T / F _____

Name _____ Date _____

"The Invalid's Story" by Mark Twain
Reading Warm-up A

Read the following passage. Pay special attention to the underlined words. Then, read it again, and complete the activities. Use a separate sheet of paper for your written answers.

Traveling by train in the late 1800s could be a grand experience or an awful one. It all depended on what kind of <u>railway</u> car you were riding in. If you were in a Pullman train car, you could expect <u>considerable</u> luxury and a great deal of service.

The inventor George Mortimer Pullman introduced his Pullman Sleeping Car in 1857. It was Pullman's <u>ambition</u> to design a railroad car that would be comfortable for overnight travel. His desire was to offer travelers the good night's sleep that earlier sleeping cars did not provide.

In 1865, a Pullman Sleeping Car was attached to the funeral train carrying President Abraham Lincoln's body to his home in Springfield, Illinois. The country was <u>distressed</u> at Lincoln's death. Those who came out to pay their respects were upset, but even so, they noticed Pullman's car. He gained fame and his business took off.

Four years later, he introduced his Pullman Palace Car. It is easy to understand why anyone lucky enough to ride in a Palace Car was <u>impressed</u>. Who would not admire a railroad car with leather seats, lamps with silk shades, and chandeliers? Who would not enjoy a delicious meal expertly served in an elegant setting?

Naturally, just about everyone would have preferred to ride in a Pullman car, but only the wealthy could afford it. For the rest, a long train ride could be a very <u>cheerless</u> experience. Hard seats, poor food, and bad smells awaited those without the money for better. Even worse, coal stoves and gas lanterns were still widely used within the wooden passenger cars. There was a constant risk of fire.

The heat could also be unbearable. Most trains had sliding windows to let in air. However, cars near the engine were showered with embers from the locomotive's smokestack, so their windows were kept closed. Woe to the passengers in those <u>stifling</u> cars on a hot day in summer. They would be <u>drenched</u> in sweat, feeling soaked and wilted. Meanwhile, the Pullman passengers were cool and fresh in their well ventilated car!

1. Circle the best clue to <u>railway</u>. Describe a time you rode in a *railway* car or saw one.

2. Underline words that are clues to <u>considerable</u>. Give a synonym for *considerable*.

3. Underline the word that is a clue to <u>ambition</u>. Explain an *ambition* you have.

4. Circle the words that are clues to <u>distressed</u>. Give an antonym for *distressed*.

5. Underline the sentences that explain why the Pullman Palace Car <u>impressed</u> people. Why would people be *impressed* by you?

6. Underline the sentence that describes a <u>cheerless</u> train ride. Give a synonym for *cheerless*.

7. Circle the clue to <u>stifling</u>. Underline the season that is often *stifling*, and then use both the word and the season in a sentence.

8. Circle the word that means the same as <u>drenched</u>. If someone on a train were *drenched* in cologne, what would you notice?

Unit 2 Resources: Short Stories
© Pearson Education, Inc., publishing as Pearson Prentice Hall. All rights reserved.

163

Name _____ Date _____

"The Invalid's Story" by Mark Twain
Reading Warm-up B

Read the following passage. Pay special attention to the underlined words. Then, read it again, and complete the activities. Use a separate sheet of paper for your written answers.

A chance meeting between Mark Twain and Ulysses S. Grant developed into a lasting friendship. It was also a profitable one for both, thanks to a book that became Twain's <u>remembrance</u> of the Union commander and president. Twain honored Grant's life by making it possible for Grant to present his autobiography and for others to read it after Grant's death.

In 1884, Grant was practically bankrupt. He was a great general but <u>pathetic</u> when it came to finances, as his judgment was very poor in business matters. When he was approached about writing a memoir, Grant was very interested because he needed the money.

Enter Mark Twain. He knew that an autobiography by Grant was <u>overdue</u>. Many readers had long expected a book by Grant. Twain knew that Grant could make more money from his life story than he had been offered, so Twain proposed to publish the book himself. Grant gladly entered into a <u>consultation</u> with Twain, and the two men discussed and agreed on a deal.

About that time, Grant began to <u>detect</u> a problem in his throat—an irritation that he noticed. He was examined by a doctor and diagnosed with inoperable cancer. Grant had no time to waste. He quietly left New York City, where he lived, and <u>placidly</u> took up residence in a mountain cabin. In that peaceful setting, he wrote of the Civil War. Reliving the <u>sufferings</u> of his soldiers and common people must have been increasingly difficult as his own pain and distress from the spreading cancer grew.

Grant's autobiography was ready for printing on July 18, 1885; five days later, he was dead. Julia Grant had always been close to her husband, and losing him must have been <u>unendurable</u>. Although nothing could soothe her misery and help her tolerate that loss, Twain was able to end her financial woes. He paid her nearly $450,000 from sales of the memoir. For the rest of his life, he was proud of having helped U. S. Grant publish his extraordinary story.

1. Underline the sentence that gives a clue to <u>remembrance</u>. Name a holiday that is about *remembrance*, and why.

2. Underline the phrase that explains why Grant's finances were <u>pathetic</u>. Give an antonym for *pathetic*.

3. Underline the phrase that gives clues to the meaning of <u>overdue</u>. If Grant was already writing and his book was *overdue*, what would that mean?

4. Underline the phrase that tells what happened during the <u>consultation</u>. In your own words, define *consultation*.

5. Circle the word that gives a clue to <u>detect</u>. What senses do you use to *detect*? Explain.

6. Circle words that give clues to <u>placidly</u>. Describe how someone might live *placidly* in the mountains.

7. Circle the phrase that gives a clue to <u>sufferings</u>. How were Grant's *sufferings* similar to those he was writing about?

8. Underline the phrase that describes an <u>unendurable</u> loss. Describe something that is *unendurable* for most people.

"The Invalid's Story" by Mark Twain
Literary Analysis: Dialogue and Dialect

Dialogue is a conversation between or among characters in a literary work. In prose, dialogue is usually set off by quotation marks, and a new paragraph indicates a change in speaker. Writers use dialogue to

- reveal character traits and relationships.
- advance the action of the plot and to develop the conflict.
- add variety, color, and realism to narratives.

To make characters even more vivid and to help establish a story's setting, authors may write dialogue that reflects characters' dialect. **Dialect** is a way of speaking that is common to people of a particular region or group. A dialect's words, pronunciations, and grammar are different from those used in the standard form of a language. In the dialect of the American South, for example, speakers often do not pronounce the *g* at the ends of *-ing* words. Dialect often makes characters' personalities, as well as the setting of a story, more vivid.

A. DIRECTIONS: *Briefly explain what each passage of dialogue from the story reveals about the speaker.*

1. "We're all right, now! I reckon we've got the Commodore this time. I judge I've got the stuff here that'll take the tuck out of him."

   _____

   _____

2. "Cap, I'm a-going to chance him once more—just this once; and if we don't fetch him this time, the thing for us to do, is to just throw up the sponge and withdraw from the canvass. That's the way *I* put it up."

   _____

   _____

   _____

B. DIRECTIONS: *Use standard English to rewrite each of the passages in dialect.*

1. "'Man that is born of woman is of few days and far between, as Scriptur' says.'"

   _____

2. "'Yes'ndeedy, it's awful solemn and cur'us; but we've all got to go, one time or another; they ain't no getting around it.'"

   _____

   _____

Name _____ Date _____

Reading: Visualize the Action to Analyze Cause and Effect

A **cause** is an event, action, or feeling that produces a result. An **effect** is the result produced. When reading a story, **visualize the action to analyze cause and effect.** Examining these relationships helps you follow the logic that drives the plot of a story.

- Based on details in the text, picture the setting, the characters, and the action.
- Use the details of your mental picture to help you identify the relationships between actions and events.

A. DIRECTIONS: *Use the lines provided to answer the following questions about cause-and-effect relationships in "The Invalid's Story."*

1. What is the effect on the narrator of his friend's death?

   _____

2. A. What causes the narrator to rush out from the eating room to the express car?

   _____

   B. What effect, unknown to the narrator at the time, results from confusion about the long white-pine boxes that are to be shipped by train?

   _____

3. As the train departs, a stranger places a package of Limburger cheese on one end of the coffin-box. What are the effects of this event?

   _____

   _____

4. A. What causes an evil odor to spread throughout the express car?

   _____

   B. What effects does the odor have on the narrator and the expressman?

   _____

B. DIRECTIONS: *Which part of the story created the most vivid impression in you? Describe and explain your choice on the lines below.*

_____

_____

_____

_____

_____

_____

"The Invalid's Story" by Mark Twain
Vocabulary Builder

Word List

prodigious	deleterious	judicious	placidly

A. DIRECTIONS: *In each item below, think about the meaning of the italicized word, and then answer the question.*

1. Describe someone who is acting *placidly.*

   _____

2. Does weather with *deleterious* effects tend to benefit or harm a building's exterior? Explain.

   _____

3. Would you ask advice from a person with a reputation for offering *judicious* advice? Explain.

   _____

4. How would you feel if you were climbing a *prodigious* mountain?

   _____

B. DIRECTIONS: *For each item below, write a single sentence using the words as grouped.*

1. *prodigious* and *deleterious*

   _____

   _____

2. *judicious* and *placidly*

   _____

   _____

C. DIRECTIONS: *For each numbered word, choose the word or phrase that is most nearly the same in meaning.*

____ 1. prodigious
   A. terrifying   B. astonishing   C. enormous   D. intelligent

____ 2. deleterious
   A. healthful   B. beneficial   C. damaged   D. harmful

____ 3. judicious
   A. foolish   B. stern   C. wise   D. pleasant

____ 4. placidly
   A. loudly   B. calmly   C. carefully   D. timidly

"The Invalid's Story" by Mark Twain
Support for Writing an Informal Letter

For your informal letter from Thompson's point of view, use the lines below to jot down notes under each heading.

Personality Traits of Thompson	Events and Details

Now, use your notes to write your informal letter to Thompson's friend or relative. Be sure that the details you include and the language you use are consistent with the personality traits you have listed for Thompson.

"The Invalid's Story" by Mark Twain
Support for Extend Your Learning

Listening and Speaking

Together with a partner, use the lines below to jot down notes for what each character says in the dialogue. You may want to start by having the narrator report on the reason for his train journey.

What the Narrator Says	What the Doctor Says
_____	_____
_____	_____
_____	_____
_____	_____
_____	_____
_____	_____
_____	_____

Research and Technology

Use the chart below to make notes for your photo collection about Mark Twain.

Stage of Twain's Life	Twain's Activities	Picture Resources
_____	_____	_____
_____	_____	_____
_____	_____	_____
_____	_____	_____
_____	_____	_____
_____	_____	_____
_____	_____	_____
_____	_____	_____
_____	_____	_____
_____	_____	_____

"The Invalid's Story" by Mark Twain
Enrichment: History of American Railroads

The setting for "The Invalid's Story" is the express, or baggage, car of a train running from Cleveland, Ohio, to Wisconsin. For about a century, roughly between 1850 and 1950, railroads were the principal transportation system in the United States. Air travel was unknown or uncommon during much of this period, and long-distance road travel did not become popular until the advent of the interstate highway system, which was begun in the 1950s. For most passengers and freight, railroads provided the best option for travel. Shipping large, bulky items—such as a coffin or a box loaded with guns—was reliable and relatively cheap through a company named Railway Express. It was by such a company that Thompson, the "expressman" in Twain's story, was employed.

DIRECTIONS: *Use a history text, online resources, or an encyclopedia to research the questions below. Write your answers on the lines provided.*

1. Identify two reasons for the relatively rapid expansion of railroads in the period 1840–1870.

    _____

    _____

2. What economic benefits did the expanding railroads bring to landowners and merchants during the second half of the nineteenth century?

    _____

    _____

    _____

3. When and where was the first transcontinental railroad line completed?

    _____

    _____

4. How did the inventions of George M. Pullman and George Westinghouse contribute to passenger comfort and safety in railroad travel?

    _____

    _____

    _____

5. What are two factors that led to the decline of American railroads in the latter part of the twentieth century?

    _____

    _____

"Blues Ain't No Mockin Bird" by Toni Cade Bambara
"The Invalid's Story" by Mark Twain
Build Language Skills: Vocabulary

Word Roots

The Latin root -*sequi-* means "to follow." For example, a *sequence* is "a following of one thing after another." One adjectival form that uses this root is *sequent*, which means "following as a result of" or "effect." Remember that words with this root will be based on the idea of following.

Example: The character gets lost in the mountains and the *sequent* action is frightening.

A. DIRECTIONS: *Use a dictionary to look up the origin of each of the following words. Then, write a sentence using the word in a context that makes its meaning clear.*

1. sequential
_____

2. consecutive
_____

3. persecute
_____

4. consequential
_____

5. non sequitur
_____

Academic Vocabulary Practice

B. DIRECTIONS: *Follow the instructions to write sentences containing the italicized Academic Vocabulary words.*

1. Use *topic* in a sentence about a magazine article.
_____

2. Use *attitude* in a sentence about a character in a literary work.
_____

3. Use *imply* in a sentence about lines from a poem.
_____

4. Use *verify* in a sentence about a scientific experiment.
_____

5. Use *sequence* in a sentence about making or breaking a code.
_____

"Blues Ain't No Mockin Bird" by Toni Cade Bambara
"The Invalid's Story" by Mark Twain
Build Language Skills: Grammar

Subject and Predicate

A. DIRECTIONS: *Write the answers to each of the following questions on the lines provided.*

1. What is the *subject* of a sentence?

   _____

   _____

2. Write an original sentence and underline the complete subject.

   _____

   _____

3. What is the *predicate* of a sentence?

   _____

   _____

4. Write an original sentence and underline the complete predicate.

   _____

   _____

5. What general rule applies to the agreement of subjects and verbs? State the rule in your own words on the lines below.

   _____

   _____

B. DIRECTIONS: *Read the following sentences and note the verbs in italics. Then, draw a vertical line in each sentence to separate the subject from the predicate.*

1. The man with the camera *cut* across our neighbor's yard.
2. Imitating Granny, Cathy *told* us a story about Goldilocks.
3. Granddaddy Cain *watched* the circles of the hawk and carefully *aimed* his hammer.
4. You *could hear* the squish of Granddaddy's boots from inside the house.
5. I *reached* home just after dark.
6. A plain man of fifty, the expressman named Thompson *was* already inside the car.
7. This recognition of my poor friend *gratified* me.
8. My health *was* permanently *shattered*.

Name _____ Date _____

Critical Reading *Identify the letter of the choice that best answers the question.*

____ 1. Which of the following is the setting for "The Invalid's Story"?
   A. a restaurant in Cleveland, Ohio
   B. a farmhouse in a small Wisconsin town
   C. a train from Cleveland to Wisconsin
   D. a lakeside park in Chicago

____ 2. Who is the invalid referred to in the story's title, "The Invalid's Story"?
   A. the narrator
   B. Thompson, the expressman
   C. the narrator's friend
   D. a stranger on the train

____ 3. The plot of "The Invalid's Story" centers on confusion about
   A. how long the narrator's friend has been dead.
   B. what is in the long white-pine box.
   C. what is in the stranger's bag.
   D. how the narrator lost his health.

____ 4. What literary element does this passage from "The Invalid's Story" illustrate?
   "Pfew! I reckon it ain't no cinnamon't I've loaded up thish-year stove with!"

   A. simile
   B. symbol
   C. flashback
   D. dialect

____ 5. In "The Invalid's Story," Mark Twain uses dialect
   A. only at the beginning and at the end.
   B. in the narrator's comments.
   C. in Deacon Hackett's dialogue.
   D. in Thompson's dialogue.

____ 6. In "The Invalid's Story," which word best describes how the narrator feels when he begins to smell the foul odor in the railroad car?
   A. curious
   B. embarrassed
   C. angry
   D. amused

_____ 7. In "The Invalid's Story," Thompson gives a long speech about the fact that death is inevitable for all human beings. Why do you think Twain includes this long speech?

    A. It shows that Thompson is a brilliant philosopher.

    B. It adds humor because it is filled with repetition and clichés.

    C. It shows that Thompson sharply disagrees with the narrator.

    D. It emphasizes the characters' sense of pleasant relaxation on their trip.

_____ 8. An idiom is a phrase or expression not meant to be taken literally. Dialects are often rich in idioms. Read the following excerpt from "The Invalid's Story."

> "Well-a-well, we've all got to go, <u>they ain't no getting around it</u>."

Which of the following best expresses the meaning of the underlined words?

    A. There is no point in going around in circles.

    B. There are ways to avoid it.

    C. There is no way to avoid it.

    D. Jumping over it is easy for some people.

_____ 9. Visualizing the action in this passage from "The Invalid's Story" allows you to appreciate which literary element at this point in the story?

> We went in again after we were frozen pretty stiff; but my, we couldn't stay in, now. So we just waltzed back and forth, freezing and thawing, and stifling, by turns.

    A. foreshadowing

    B. metaphor

    C. dialogue

    D. humor

_____ 10. In "The Invalid's Story," why do the two men light up cigars?

    A. The cigars were a present to the narrator from the dead man.

    B. The men want to "modify" the unpleasant odor in the expressman's car.

    C. The men are trying to keep warm and think smoking might help.

    D. The engineer has requested that the men smoke cigars.

_____ 11. Visualize the action in this passage from Twain's story. What is the cause of the action?

> He gagged and gasped, and floundered up and made a break for the door, pawing the air and saying hoarsely, "Don't hender me!—gimme the road! I'm a dying; gimme the road!"

    A. Thompson probably has a bad case of food poisoning.

    B. Thompson is a person who likes to exaggerate whatever he is feeling.

    C. The smell in the railroad car is becoming increasingly unbearable.

    D. The railroad car has finally reached its destination.

____ **12.** The narrator of "The Invalid's Story" says that "the news was too late to save me; imagination had done its work, and my health was permanently shattered." According to the narrator, what has caused the permanent breakdown in his health?

    A. imagination

    B. overwork

    C. infection

    D. ambition

Vocabulary and Grammar

____ **13.** What is the best synonym for *prodigious* as it is used in this sentence?

    The fact is that without my suspecting it a prodigious mistake had been made.

    A. modest   **C.** huge

    B. tiny   **D.** rebellious

____ **14.** Which word is most nearly opposite in meaning to *judicious* in this sentence?

    It seemed judicious to enlarge the facts to fit the probabilities.

    A. silent   **C.** abundant

    B. unreasonable   **D.** miraculous

____ **15.** Which of these does the complete predicate of a sentence always contain?

    A. an adverb   **C.** the verb

    B. the subject   **D.** a prepositional phrase

Essay

16. In an essay, describe how Twain uses images of smell in "The Invalid's Story" to create the story's humor. Mention one specific example from the story.

17. Dialect is a way of speaking that is common to people of a particular region or group. In an essay, discuss Mark Twain's use of dialect in "The Invalid's Story." Where, specifically, does Twain use dialect in the story? How does dialect add to the story's vivid setting and its humor?

"The Invalid's Story" by Mark Twain
Selection Test B

Critical Reading *Identify the letter of the choice that best completes the statement or answers the question.*

_____ 1. Confusion underlies the plot of "The Invalid's Story." About whom or what are the characters confused?
   A. the circumstances of the friend's death
   B. the exact contents of the box
   C. the final destination of the train
   D. how the narrator became ill

_____ 2. In "The Invalid's Story," the person who dies is
   A. Deacon Levi Hackett.
   B. the expressman Thompson.
   C. John B. Hackett.
   D. Cap, the narrator.

_____ 3. Which of the following is the setting for "The Invalid's Story"?
   A. a farmhouse in rural Wisconsin
   B. a train journey from Chicago, Illinois, to Cleveland, Ohio
   C. a train journey from Cleveland, Ohio, to Wisconsin
   D. a waiting room in the train station at Peoria, Illinois

_____ 4. What literary element does this sentence from "The Invalid's Story" illustrate?
   "Pfew! I reckon it ain't no cinnamon't I've loaded up thish-year stove with!"
   A. metaphor
   B. foreshadowing
   C. setting
   D. dialect

_____ 5. Why does Mark Twain choose to set "The Invalid's Story" in winter?
   A. to create a cozy mood
   B. to describe how the narrator's friend died
   C. to provide more opportunity for exaggeration
   D. to explain why the train ride was slow

_____ 6. In "The Invalid's Story," in which parts of the tale does Mark Twain use dialect?
   A. in the narrator's descriptions of the setting
   B. in the flashback passages in which the narrator remembers his friend
   C. in the narrator's dialogue with his friend's family
   D. in Thompson's dialogue with the narrator

_____ 7. Twain probably included Thompson's monologue on the inevitability of death in order to
   A. show that Thompson is shockingly prejudiced.
   B. increase the humorous irony of the scene.
   C. foreshadow Thompson's own illness and death.
   D. stress that Thompson has a great reservoir of common sense.

_____ 8. An idiom is a phrase or expression not meant to be taken literally. Dialects are often rich in idioms. Which of the following best expresses the underlined idiom from Twain's story?

"Well-a-well, we've all got to go, they ain't no getting around it."

A. It's a situation that only a very few people can manage to avoid.
B. If you think hard enough, you will find a way to postpone it.
C. You simply have to accept the fact that it's inevitable.
D. Some people—but not everyone—can manage to cope with it.

_____ 9. In "The Invalid's Story," the two men are motivated to smoke cigars because
A. the cigars remind them of the narrator's dead friend, who always smoked cigars.
B. the men want to "modify" the foul odor in the expressman's car.
C. the engineer has specifically requested that they not smoke while on the train.
D. the men hope that the cigars will warm them up.

_____ 10. In "The Invalid's Story," what point of view does Mark Twain use?
A. first-person
B. third-person limited
C. third-person omniscient
D. objective

_____ 11. Visualizing the action in this passage from "The Invalid's Story" allows you to appreciate which of the following literary elements at this point in the story?

We went in again after we were frozen pretty stiff; but my, we couldn't stay in, now. So we just waltzed back and forth, freezing and thawing, and stifling, by turns.

A. personification
B. metaphor
C. refrain
D. humor

_____ 12. In "The Invalid's Story," from the narrator's point of view the situation in the express car is
A. hilarious.
B. embarrassing.
C. paradoxical.
D. comfortable.

_____ 13. According to the narrator in "The Invalid's Story," the permanent breakdown in his health is due to
A. a hyperactive imagination.
B. overexposure to the cold.
C. exposure to a contagious disease.
D. a compromised immune system.

___ 14. Which sentence from "The Invalid's Story" creates an image that appeals to your sense of hearing?

A. Presently I began to detect a most evil and searching odor on the frozen air.

B. Just then the conductor sang out "All aboard."

C. Thompson sat down and buried his face in his red silk handkerchief.

D. We puffed gingerly along for a while, and tried hard to imagine that things were improved.

Vocabulary and Grammar

___ 15. Which word best defines *deleterious*?

A. careless   C. harmful

B. lengthy   D. miserable

___ 16. Which word is most nearly opposite in meaning to *prodigious* in this sentence?

The fact is that without my suspecting it a prodigious mistake had been made.

A. prophetic   C. tiny

B. prudent   D. insensible

___ 17. What is the complete predicate of this sentence?

Most of the passengers on the train slept through the journey.

A. Most of the passengers   C. slept through the journey

B. on the train   D. through the journey

___ 18. A line drawn to separate the subject and the predicate in this sentence would come after which word?

We sat some time, in meditative silence, listening to the wind and the roar of the train.

A. We   C. silence

B. time   D. wind

Essay

19. In an essay, describe the use of images of smell in "The Invalid's Story." Explain why the images of smell are humorous and how Thompson's reactions to the smells add to the story's humor.

20. The narrator in "The Invalid's Story," in order to transport the body of a friend, travels in an express car on a two-hundred-mile train journey that takes an entire night. The element of pacing in a story relates to the way in which the plot unfolds. In an essay, discuss how Mark Twain uses pacing in the story to increase suspense, exaggeration, and humor as the train journey continues to the final destination.

Vocabulary Warm-up Word Lists

Study these words from the stories. Then, complete the activities.

Word List A

accidentally [ak suh DEN tuh lee] *adv.* not purposely; unexpectedly
I did not see her on the darkened stairwell and <u>accidentally</u> bumped into her.

awkwardness [AWK werd nes] *n.* movement that is not comfortable; clumsiness
Her <u>awkwardness</u> on the dance floor made her feel out of place at the party.

discouraged [dis KER ijd] *adj.* made less hopeful or confident
The players were <u>discouraged</u> by the coach's constant criticism.

exotic [eg ZAH tik] *adj.* unusual; strange; foreign
At the zoo, we saw <u>exotic</u> animals from all over the world.

hazy [HAY zee] *adj.* misty or unclear
The committee had only a <u>hazy</u> idea of how to achieve its goals.

monotony [muh NAHT uh nee] *n.* sameness; boredom
The <u>monotony</u> of working on the assembly line left her bored and restless.

spectacular [spek TAK yuh ler] *adj.* impressive; very exciting
We were thrilled by the actor's <u>spectacular</u> performance.

unbearable [uhn BAIR uh buhl] *adj.* too uncomfortable or painful to deal with
I walked out of the scary movie when the tension became <u>unbearable</u>.

Word List B

bustling [BUHS ling] *adj.* noisy and active
They left the <u>bustling</u> city for the quiet of the country.

cooperation [koh ah puh RAY shuhn] *n.* act of working together
With a little <u>cooperation</u>, we can get the job done.

departed [di PAR tid] *v.* left
They stayed at the party for an hour and then <u>departed</u>.

modesty [MOD is tee] *n.* reluctance to talk proudly about one's achievements
Her <u>modesty</u> prevented her from bragging about her success.

omens [OH minz] *n.* signs of future events
His excellent test scores were <u>omens</u> of great things to come.

paralyzed [PAR uh lyzd] *adj.* helpless; unable to move
He was <u>paralyzed</u> with fear and lay perfectly still.

quench [KWENCH] *v.* put out
To <u>quench</u> the last sparks of the fire, we threw sand over the coals.

sustain [suh STAYN] *v.* support; maintain; keep up
His excellent study habits helped him <u>sustain</u> his good grades.

"The Scarlet Ibis" by James Hurst
"The Golden Kite, the Silver Wind" by Ray Bradbury
Vocabulary Warm-up Exercises

Exercise A *Fill in the blanks using each word from Word List A only once.*

We arrived in London on a hot and [1] _____ summer morning.
We had lunch that day in a street lined with Indian, Ethiopian, and other
[2] _____ restaurants. I was a little [3] _____ by all the
strange-sounding items on the menu, but I ordered a delicious vegetable dish. After
lunch, we went to the Tower of London to see the Crown Jewels. They were truly
[4] _____, but I was so embarrassed when I [5] _____
bumped into one of the guards! I was relieved that my [6] _____ did not
get me in trouble. When the afternoon heat grew [7] _____, we returned
to our hotel room. The week passed quickly. There were so many things to do that I did
not want to return to the [8] _____ of my daily life!

Exercise B *Answer the questions with complete explanations.*

1. Would someone who dislikes noise want to live in a *bustling* community?
   _____

2. Does *cooperation* make a project get finished more quickly or more slowly?
   _____

3. If a train *departed* ahead of schedule, is it likely to arrive at its destination earlier or
   later than planned?
   _____

4. Can people brag about their own *modesty*?
   _____

5. If a fortuneteller sees *omens* of disaster, does he or she expect good things to
   happen?
   _____

6. What would you do to *quench* a bonfire?
   _____

7. If you want to *sustain* your good reputation, what should you do?
   _____

8. If someone is *paralyzed* by fear, is he or she likely to take instant action?
   _____

"The Scarlet Ibis" by James Hurst
"The Golden Kite, the Silver Wind" by Ray Bradbury
Reading Warm-up A

Read the following passage. Pay special attention to the underlined words. Then, read it again, and complete the activities. Use a separate sheet of paper for your written answers.

My kid brother Jason was never like the other kids in the neighborhood. You know how most little kids act all squirrelly and do not know what to say when grownups are around? Jason never showed the slightest signs of discomfort around grownups or anyone else.

Jason never complained about anything, either. I remember when I taught him how to ride a bicycle; it makes me smile to think about his childish <u>awkwardness</u> then. He must have fallen off that bike a hundred times, but he never got <u>discouraged</u>. Anyone else would have wanted to quit, but Jason was not like anyone else. He was like an <u>exotic</u> creature that thrived in an alien environment.

School was never a problem for my little brother. He was never bothered by the <u>monotony</u> of going to class every day and doing homework every night. You might surmise that he was some kind of obnoxious bookworm, but you would be wrong. Everyone loved Jason and he loved everyone right back. If he <u>accidentally</u> hurt someone's feelings with a careless word or deed, Jason would immediately write that person a beautiful letter of apology so that nobody ever stayed angry with him. When he flashed his <u>spectacular</u> smile at you, you just wanted to take the little guy in your arms and give him a great big hug. Jason could be so lovable sometimes that it was almost <u>unbearable</u>.

My memory of when it all began to change is a little <u>hazy</u>, but I think it was around the time he started high school. Adolescence seemed to make Jason grouchy. Sometimes, he would get into an argument with a classmate or complain about school or even forget to do his homework. When I saw the changes begin, I was sure the kid was in for some serious trouble.

I was wrong, however. Jason's enchanted childhood had finally come to an end. Now he was just like all the other kids in the neighborhood—and that turned out to be no great tragedy after all!

1. Underline the words that show Jason's <u>awkwardness</u>. What might *awkwardness* cause a person to do?

2. Circle the words that tell what someone who was <u>discouraged</u> might do. What might cause a person to feel *discouraged*?

3. Circle the word that hints at the meaning of <u>exotic</u>. Why does the narrator compare Jason to an *exotic* creature?

4. Underline the words that tell what the narrator thinks of as <u>monotony</u>. Then, explain what *monotony* means.

5. Underline the words that tell how Jason might <u>accidentally</u> hurt someone's feelings. What might someone do *accidentally*?

6. Underline the words that tell the effect of Jason's <u>spectacular</u> smile. Name something you think is *spectacular*.

7. Underline the words that tell what was sometimes <u>unbearable</u>. Then, write what *unbearable* means.

8. Circle the words that suggest that the narrator's memory is <u>hazy</u>. Write a sentence about a *hazy* memory of your own.

"The Scarlet Ibis" by James Hurst
"The Golden Kite, the Silver Wind" by Ray Bradbury
Reading Warm-up B

Read the following passage. Pay special attention to the underlined words. Then, read it again, and complete the activities. Use a separate sheet of paper for your written answers.

Imagine a wall of brick and stone, fifteen feet wide and twenty-five feet high. Imagine that it spans some 1,500 miles. That is roughly the distance from New York City to Omaha, Nebraska. Imagine a wall so vast that astronauts orbiting Earth can see it from space! Believe it or not, you have just imagined one of the seven wonders of the world—the Great Wall of China.

Built entirely by hand, the Great Wall was begun around the seventh century B.C.E. It took many hundreds of years to complete. The first segments were built thousands of years ago to keep out invaders from the north. Nearly underlined(paralyzed) by the fear of being overrun by barbarians, Chinese emperors ordered that a wall be built in order to protect the people. Not known for their underlined(modesty), these boastful emperors often bragged about the superiority of Chinese civilization. The rulers were also eager to underlined(sustain) their own power.

When nomadic Mongols entered the country through gaps in the wall, the emperors interpreted these invasions as underlined(omens) of future disaster. More walls were built to fill in the gaps. Millions of laborers were enlisted to help at the underlined(bustling) work sites that sprang up across the country. Vast quantities of water were needed to satisfy the thirst of the hardworking men and underlined(quench) the fires that sometimes started along the length of the wall. The underlined(cooperation) of countless workers was necessary to complete the vast building project.

Today, people come from all over the world to walk along the Great Wall and marvel at its beauty. Protecting the ancient wall from damage without halting tourism has been an ongoing concern for the Chinese government. Fortunately, millions of visitors have underlined(departed) from China with a greater awareness of the need to safeguard this cultural treasure for future generations.

1. Underline the words that tell what almost underlined(paralyzed) the Chinese. What does *paralyzed* mean?

2. Circle the word that suggests the opposite of underlined(modesty). Describe someone who shows great *modesty* about his or her achievements.

3. Circle the words that tell what the emperors wanted to underlined(sustain). Then, explain what *sustain* means.

4. Explain why the emperors saw the invasions as underlined(omens). Then, tell what *omens* are.

5. Circle the words that tell what was underlined(bustling). Write about a *bustling* place in your community.

6. Explain why water would underlined(quench) a fire. Write about a time when you had to *quench* something.

7. Underline the words that tell what underlined(cooperation) was necessary to do. Write about something else that requires *cooperation.*

8. Circle the word that tells from where the visitors underlined(departed). Then, write a sentence using a word that means the opposite of *departed.*

"The Scarlet Ibis" by James Hurst
"The Golden Kite, the Silver Wind" by Ray Bradbury

Literary Analysis: Symbol and Allegory

A **symbol** is a person, a place, a thing, or an event that represents both itself and a larger idea or feeling. **Symbolism** is the use of symbols in literature. For example, a writer might use a journey as a symbol for the life of a human being.

An **allegory** is a poem or story that has parallel literal and symbolic meanings. On the literal level, the story appears simply as it is told. On the symbolic level, however, every element in the story—including the characters, events, descriptions, and features of the setting—has a symbolic meaning. While an allegory can be understood on the literal level, its full meaning is clear only on the symbolic level. Often, allegories may seem less realistic than nonallegorical works, and they may shed light on current events.

DIRECTIONS: *After you have read the selections, think about which of each work's details and events may be symbolic or allegorical. Then, read these key passages from the stories, and answer the questions that follow.*

"The Scarlet Ibis"

1. That summer, the summer of 1918, was blighted. In May and June there was no rain and the crops withered, curled up, then died under the thirsty sun.

   What is symbolic about the weather in this passage?

   _____

   _____

   _____

2. For a long long time, it seemed forever, I lay there crying, sheltering my fallen scarlet ibis from the heresy of rain.

   How is the symbolism in this passage related to a central theme or insight in the story?

   _____

   _____

   _____

"The Golden Kite, the Silver Wind"

3. And on every night of the year the inhabitants of the Town of the Kite could hear the good clear wind sustaining them. And those in the Town of the Wind could hear the kite singing, whispering, rising, and beautifying them.

   How does this outcome suggest the moral lesson to be drawn from the allegory in this story?

   _____

   _____

   _____

"The Scarlet Ibis" by James Hurst
"The Golden Kite, the Silver Wind" by Ray Bradbury
Vocabulary Builder

Word List

imminent	infallibility	precariously	vile	ravenous	spurn

A. DIRECTIONS: *Revise each sentence so that the underlined vocabulary word is used logically. Be sure not to change the vocabulary word.*

1. A thunderstorm appears to be <u>imminent</u>, so we have decided to stay in the pool.

   _____

2. Josh made so many errors on the math test that we marveled at his <u>infallibility</u>.

   _____

3. A baby spider monkey is dangling <u>precariously</u> from the top of that tall tree, so we are not worried about its safety.

   _____

   _____

4. The crime was so <u>vile</u> that the judge gave the convicted defendant a suspended sentence.

   _____

5. That tiger ate so little meat! It must have been <u>ravenous</u>.

   _____

6. To <u>spurn</u> a fellow guest at a party is a good way to make a new friend.

   _____

B. DIRECTIONS: *Write the letter of the word that is the best antonym of the Word List word.*

___ 1. precariously
   A. dangerously
   B. securely
   C. insecurely
   D. ridiculously

___ 2. vile
   A. disgusting
   B. evil
   C. good
   D. upsetting

___ 3. ravenous
   A. polite
   B. full
   C. nervous
   D. pleasant

___ 4. spurn
   A. welcome
   B. reject
   C. introduce
   D. insult

Name _____ Date _____

"The Scarlet Ibis" by James Hurst
"The Golden Kite, the Silver Wind" by Ray Bradbury
Writing to Compare Literary Works

Use a chart like the one shown to make prewriting notes for your essay comparing and contrasting the use of symbolism in the two stories.

Points of Comparison/Contrast	"The Scarlet Ibis"	"The Golden Kite, the Silver Wind"
Message or lesson expressed in story		
Use of symbols to develop message		
If symbols were omitted, how would the message change?		

Name _____ Date _____

Critical Reading *Identify the letter of the choice that best answers the question.*

____ 1. In "The Scarlet Ibis," why does the narrator rename his little brother Doodle?

    A. People expect too much of someone named William Armstrong.

    B. The little boy does not like to be called William Armstrong.

    C. The little boy crawls backward like a doodle-bug.

    D. Doodle is an old family nickname.

____ 2. What prompts the narrator to show Doodle the coffin?

    A. The narrator thinks that Doodle will find it amusing.

    B. He intends to shut Doodle up inside the coffin as a joke.

    C. He has a cruel streak that surfaces occasionally.

    D. He wants to impress on Doodle how surprised they all were that Doodle survived.

____ 3. In literature, what is the correct term for a person, a place, a thing, or an event that represents both itself and a larger idea or feeling?

    A. allegory

    B. epic

    C. symbol

    D. simile

____ 4. What is the main lesson of the relationship of the two brothers in "The Scarlet Ibis"?

    A. how to appreciate a brother or sister

    B. how to design a lying contest

    C. how to teach someone to walk

    D. how to tease a brother or sister

____ 5. Who or what is the main symbol in "The Scarlet Ibis"?

    A. Doodle

    B. death

    C. the scarlet ibis

    D. the seasons

____ 6. In "The Golden Kite, the Silver Wind," how do the townspeople eventually respond to rebuilding the wall over and over again?

   A. They become weak or ill, and many die.

   B. They enjoy the competition between the two towns.

   C. They build walls during the day and run their farms and businesses at night.

   D. They rebel and refuse to build any more walls.

____ 7. In "The Golden Kite, the Silver Wind," how does the daughter help her father and Kwan-Si see the solution to the problem?

   A. She forces them to eat a meal together and be friendly.

   B. She gives each one of them a kite to fly.

   C. She takes them outside to see how kites and the wind go together.

   D. She makes them talk to some children who are flying kites.

____ 8. Why may "The Golden Kite, the Silver Wind" be called an allegory?

   A. The story has a happy ending.

   B. The story has a remote, exotic setting.

   C. The story has parallel literal and symbolic meanings.

   D. The story includes several elements of fantasy.

____ 9. Which is the best comparison of "The Scarlet Ibis" and "The Golden Kite, the Silver Wind"?

   A. Both stories are told from the first-person point of view.

   B. In both stories, the main character may be described as cruel.

   C. The titles of both stories contain important symbols.

   D. Both stories use dialect, or regional speech, in the dialogue of the characters.

____ 10. In which story (or stories) does the main symbol represent a specific person?

   A. in "The Scarlet Ibis"

   B. in "The Golden Kite, the Silver Wind"

   C. in both stories

   D. in neither story

____ 11. Which line most clearly indicates what the scarlet ibis symbolizes?

   A. At that moment the bird began to flutter, but the wings were uncoordinated. . . .

   B. Its long, graceful neck jerked twice into an S, then it straightened out, and the bird was still.

   C. Even death did not mar its grace, for it lay on the earth like a broken vase of red flowers. . . .

   D. For a long time, it seemed forever, I lay there crying, sheltering my fallen scarlet ibis from the heresy of rain.

Vocabulary

____ 12. If an event is <u>imminent</u>, how might you describe it?
A. as irreversible
B. as likely to happen soon
C. as possible but not probable
D. as impossible

____ 13. Which of the following might reasonably be described as <u>vile</u>?
A. a birthday
B. a violent crime
C. a practical joke
D. a suspenseful film

____ 14. Which phrase most nearly means <u>ravenous</u>?
A. very hungry
B. extremely thirsty
C. thoroughly bored
D. hysterically funny

Essay

15. A symbol is a person, a place, a thing, or an event that represents both itself and a larger idea or feeling. In both "The Scarlet Ibis" and "The Golden Kite, the Silver Wind," symbols play an important role. Choose either story, and in an essay explain how symbolism is related to the story's plot and central message.

16. Both the narrator in "The Scarlet Ibis" and the Mandarin in "The Golden Kite, the Silver Wind" are complex, dynamic characters. In an essay, discuss how each character has a number of different, conflicting traits. Also, show how both characters grow and change in the course of the stories.

"The Scarlet Ibis" by James Hurst
"The Golden Kite, the Silver Wind" by Ray Bradbury
Selection Test B

Critical Reading *Identify the letter of the choice that best completes the statement or answers the question.*

____ 1. In "The Scarlet Ibis," why is the narrator's brother three months old before he is named?
    A. His parents cannot agree on a name.
    B. It is traditional to wait three months before naming a baby.
    C. Everybody thinks that the baby will die.
    D. The baby first has to be baptized in the church.

____ 2. Once Doodle has learned to walk, what motivates the narrator to persist with Doodle's development program?
    A. his belief in his own infallibility
    B. his belief in Doodle's infallibility
    C. his sympathy for Doodle
    D. his defiance of his parents

____ 3. Which passage from "The Scarlet Ibis" best illustrates a feeling of triumph?
    A. . . . I put him on his feet at least a hundred times each afternoon.
    B. "And before I'll help you down from the loft, you're going to have to touch it."
    C. Finally, I could see I was licked. Doodle was my brother and he was going to cling to me forever.
    D. There wasn't a sound as Doodle walked slowly across the room and sat down at his place at the table.

____ 4. In "The Scarlet Ibis," with which character is the bird in the story's title symbolically associated?
    A. the narrator
    B. Mama
    C. Aunt Nicey
    D. Doodle

____ 5. In "The Scarlet Ibis," how does the weather contribute to the atmosphere, or mood?
    A. The weather creates a mood of confinement.
    B. The weather seems reliable and reassuring.
    C. The weather seems threatening and unpredictable.
    D. The weather creates a feeling of lightheartedness.

____ 6. Which passage from "The Scarlet Ibis" conveys a feeling of optimism?
    A. Hope no longer hid in the dark palmetto thicket but perched like a cardinal in the lacy toothbrush tree, brilliantly visible.
    B. Then when the slanted rays of the sun burned orange in the tops of the pines, we'd drop our jewels into the stream and watch them float away toward the sea.
    C. But sometimes (like right now), as I sit in the cool, green-draped parlor, the grindstone begins to turn, and time with all its changes is ground away. . . .
    D. . . . The peacock spread his magnificent tail, enfolding the boy gently like a closing go-to-sleep flower, burying him in the gloriously iridescent, rustling vortex.

____ 7. In "The Golden Kite, the Silver Wind," why is the Mandarin upset when Kwan-Si builds his wall in the shape of a pig?
   A. He believes the shape of the wall is a portent.
   B. He thinks a pig shape is undignified for a town's wall.
   C. He wants his own wall to be in the shape of a pig.
   D. He believes Kwan-Si is insulting him by choosing a pig shape.

____ 8. In "The Golden Kite, the Silver Wind," once the Mandarin's daughter understands why her father is upset, what does she do?
   A. She sends a messenger to see what Kwan-Si will do next.
   B. She has her father's bed drawn up next to the silken screen.
   C. She tells her father that the towns must live together peacefully.
   D. She gives her father advice about how to "beat" Kwan-Si.

____ 9. Which of the following best defines *allegory*?
   A. a story in which readers identify with the main character
   B. a story in which foreshadowing is a prominent literary element
   C. a poem or story that has parallel literal and symbolic meanings
   D. a poem or story in which the setting is closely linked with the atmosphere, or overall mood

____ 10. How does "The Golden Kite, the Silver Wind" shed light on human nature and behavior?
   A. The story shows how fathers and daughters should treat each other.
   B. The story shows how Chinese society is structured.
   C. The story shows what happens when greedy rulers get carried away with their power.
   D. The story shows how intense rivalry can damage communities and their residents.

____ 11. Which sentence from "The Golden Kite, the Silver Wind" best states the author's theme?
   A. Like a rusted machine, the city ground to a halt.
   B. The Mandarin wept. "All is lost! These symbols and signs terrify. . . ."
   C. "One without the other is nothing. Together, all will be beauty and cooperation. . . ."
   D. "They make their walls like a sword to break your needle!"

____ 12. Which story (or stories) can be classified as an allegory?
   A. "The Scarlet Ibis"
   B. "The Golden Kite, the Silver Wind"
   C. both stories
   D. neither story

____ 13. Which statement most accurately describes the role symbols play in "The Scarlet Ibis" and "The Golden Kite, the Silver Wind"?
   A. Symbols represent a specific person in one story and abstract ideas in the other.
   B. In both stories, the symbols present vivid images of sound.
   C. In one story, the symbol is hidden; in the other, the symbols are obvious.
   D. The meaning of the symbols is not clear in either story.

Vocabulary

____ 14. If you were convinced of your own <u>infallibility</u>, which of these feelings might you have?
  A. hesitation
  B. puzzlement
  C. regret
  D. confidence

____ 15. Which description might apply to an object that was positioned <u>precariously</u>?
  A. teetering
  B. centered
  C. moldering
  D. decorated

____ 16. Which of the following might reasonably be associated with the word <u>vile</u>?
  A. mathematical proof
  B. accurate prediction
  C. outrageous crime
  D. historical account

____ 17. How do you think you would feel if your best friend suddenly decided to <u>spurn</u> you?
  A. thankful
  B. guilty
  C. shocked
  D. indifferent

Essay

18. A symbol is something that stands for or represents something else. In "The Scarlet Ibis," the scarlet ibis is a symbol for Doodle. In an essay, compare the bird and Doodle. Consider all facets of what you know about the character of Doodle as you explain this symbolism.

19. In both "The Scarlet Ibis" and "The Golden Kite, the Silver Moon," symbolism is a prominent literary element. Yet, both stories are written in quite different styles and produce a different overall effect. Choose one of the stories, and in an essay, briefly discuss the story's style. Then, analyze the ways in which symbolism contributes to the story's total effect. Support your main ideas with specific examples and references to the story.

Writing Workshop—Unit 2, Part 2
Exposition: Cause-and-Effect Essay

Prewriting: Gathering Details

Use the following graphic organizer to decide whether to explore the causes that produced a central event or the effects the event produced. List the causes and effects and note the key details related to each.

Central Event:

Cause:

Key details:

Cause:

Key details:

Cause:

Key details:

Effect:

Key details:

Effect:

Key details:

Effect:

Key details:

Drafting: Using the TRI Method

Use the chart to help you develop the paragraphs of your essay. To do this, follow the steps listed in the first column for each of your body paragraphs.

TRI Method:	Paragraph 1:	Paragraph 2:	Paragraph 3:
Topic:			
Restate your topic.			
Illustrate your point through details, facts, examples, and personal experiences.			

Writing Workshop—Unit 2, Part 2
Review of a Short Story: Integrating Grammar Skills

Revising Faulty Subject-Verb Agreement

A verb must agree with its subject in number. A compound subject (joined by *and*) is plural in number and requires a plural verb.

Compound Subject: *A salad and a baked potato* come with the dinner.

Subjects joined by *or* and *nor* are considered singular unless the *last* part is plural.

Singular Subject and Verb: Either *two vegetables or a salad* comes with the dinner.

Plural Subject and Verb: Either *a salad or two vegetables* come with the dinner.

The indefinite pronouns *each* and *one* are always singular. Indefinite pronouns, such as *both* and *many,* are always plural.

Singular Subject and Verb: *Each* of the dinners *comes* with a salad.

Plural Subject and Verb: *Both* of the dinners *come* with a salad.

Indefinite pronouns, such as *all* or *most,* may be singular or plural, depending on the nouns to which they refer.

Singular Subject and Verb: *Most* of the food *comes* with no extra charge.

Plural Subject and Verb: *Most* of the desserts *come* with the meal.

Identifying Correct Subject-Verb Agreement

A. DIRECTIONS: *Complete each sentence by circling the verb that agrees with the subject.*

1. A pine and a willow (grows, grow) at the park entrance.
2. Most of the park's trees (thrives, thrive) in cool climate.
3. Either two oaks or a maple (borders, border) the pond.
4. Most of the park (feels, feel) cool in summer.

Fixing Incorrect Subject-Verb Agreement

B. DIRECTIONS: *On the lines provided, rewrite these sentences so that the subject and verb agree in each.*

1. Funds for the school system tops the list of town expenses.

_____

2. The library and the civic center costs the town little money.

_____

3. Either fees or a special tax fund the local library.

_____

4. Each of the town board members know the details about the budget.

_____

Name _____ Date _____

Spelling Workshop—Unit 2
Tricky or Unusual Consonants

To spell some words correctly, you must be on the lookout for **unusual consonant combinations.** Examples include combinations that you do not see too often (as in _rhyme_) or combinations in which a letter is silent (as in _subtle_). Make note of such troublesome parts in the words in this list.

Word List

| acquaintance | afghan | campaign | condemn | receipt |
| adjourn | asthma | cologne | overwhelming | ricochet |

A. DIRECTIONS: _Write the word from the Word List that matches each clue._

1. a light perfume _____
2. overpowering _____
3. end the meeting _____
4. disease causing wheezing _____
5. blame _____
6. person you know _____
7. knitted or woven blanket _____
8. proof of payment _____
9. bounce off a surface _____
10. work to get votes _____

B. DIRECTIONS: _For each item, write two or three related sentences using the words listed._

1. campaign   adjourn   condemn

_____

_____

2. afghan   acquaintance   overwhelming   asthma

_____

_____

_____

3. cologne   receipt   ricochet

_____

_____

_____

Communications Workshop: Unit 2
Evaluating a Speech

After viewing a political speech or televised editorial, fill out the following chart to assess the content and delivery of the speech.

Title of political speech or televised editorial: _____

What is the speaker's purpose?
What knowledge or experience equips the speaker to address the subject?
What prior knowledge do you have about the speaker's subject?
What evidence does the speaker give to support this subject?
Is the speaker's use of facts fair and responsible or biased?
How effective are the techniques the speaker uses, such as tone of voice, eye contact, facial expressions, and so on? Explain.

For Further Reading: Unit 2

DIRECTIONS: *Think about the books you have read. Then, on a separate piece of paper, answer the discussion questions and take notes for your literature circle.*

The Sherlock Holmes Mysteries by Sir Arthur Conan Doyle

Discussion Holmes solves mysteries by taking the end result and breaking it into steps. Each step then helps him understand the events in a mystery. Trace Holmes's thinking in one of the twenty-two stories in this collection.

Connection—Literature Circle How would Holmes go about solving a crime today? What would be different? What would be the same?

To Kill a Mockingbird by Harper Lee

Discussion The neighborhood children in *To Kill a Mockingbird* are frightened of Boo Radley because he is different. How does Scout's perception of Boo change as she gets to know him? Do you think that fear of the unknown is a trait that is only found in childhood? Explain your response.

Connection—Literature Circle Atticus Finch says that a mob is "always made up of people" (page 157) Apply this idea to an event or series of events in history and judge its validity.

Literature of the Expanding Frontier Prentice Hall Anthology

Discussion Compare and contrast the way in which the Pioneer Spirit is depicted by the early authors with the way is it depicted by the modern authors. Use specific details from the works to support your comparison.

Connection—Literature Circle "We are the pioneers of the world; the advance-guard, sent on through the wilderness of untried things, to break a new path in the New World that is ours." —Herman Melville (1819–1891), *The Writings of Herman Melville*
Demonstrate how this quotation applies to one of the works in the anthology. Use specific details from the work to support your points.

The Sea Wolf and Selected Stories by Jack London

Discussion How is "survival" a recurring theme throughout each of the stories in this collection?

Connection—Literature Circle How is Wolf Larsen described in the story? How would you describe him?

Unit 2: Short Stories
Part 2 Benchmark Test 4

Literary Analysis: Character and Characterization *Read the selection. Then, answer the questions that follow.*

People who don't know Harry tend to underestimate him. They cast a skeptical eye on his typical outfit: ragged jeans and shirts that bear evidence of his most recent meal. And his most frequently uttered expression, "Waaaal, I just don't know," can make him sound less than bright. So, some enter a negotiating session with Harry relaxed and confident that their side will prevail, and that Harry will gain no concessions for his group. That assumption is one that Harry cultivates and it is a big, big mistake.

1. Which of the following details supports characterization in a short story?
   A. information and details about the time and location
   B. explanations and descriptions of the central problem
   C. details about people's appearance and personalities
   D. the main idea or insight an author wants to convey

2. Which kinds of characterization does this selection include?
   A. direct
   B. indirect
   C. direct and indirect
   D. internal

3. What kind of technique does an author use to show a character's traits through that character's dialogue?
   A. symbolism and irony
   B. point of view
   C. direct characterization.
   D. indirect characterization.

4. Which of the following reveals the most about the character in this selection?
   A. his words
   B. his appearance
   C. the setting
   D. the narrator's description

5. What is another word for the reasons behind a character's thoughts, feelings, and actions?
   A. motivations
   B. inferences
   C. quotations
   D. implications

Literary Analysis: Dialogue *Read the passage. Then, answer the questions that follow.*

"Stop checking your watch," Elise told Jessica.

Jessica quickly dropped her hand to her side. "I wasn't. I was just stretching," she replied.

"You are going to be great. There is nothing to worry about," Elise stated in a much kinder tone.

"I know. Thanks for coming with me. It means a lot," Jessica replied as she stepped out of the elevator.

6. What does the dialogue reveal about Jessica?
   A. She is nervous.
   B. She is lazy.
   C. She is energetic.
   D. She is strong.

7. Which punctuation mark signals dialogue?
   A. comma
   B. quotation mark
   C. apostrophe
   D. parenthesis

8. Based on the dialogue, where might Jessica be going?
   A. on her vacation
   B. for an interview
   C. to Elise's house
   D. to her home

9. What is the most important reason an author might have a character speak in dialect?
   A. Dialect is fun to read.
   B. Dialect makes readers pay attention to a character's words.
   C. Dialect is a way for an author to state the theme indirectly.
   D. Dialect reveals characters and setting vividly.

Literary Analysis: Symbolism and Allegory

10. Which of the following statements about symbolism and allegory is correct?
    A. A story may employ symbolism but still not be an allegory.
    B. An allegory never includes symbols.
    C. Without symbolism, an allegory would be more effective.
    D. Stories that are not allegories use different kinds of symbols.

11. Which of the following might be used by an author as a symbol for new life and hope?
    A. a river
    B. springtime
    C. a driveway
    D. a newspaper

12. In literature, what does a sunset often symbolize?
    A. a beginning
    B. day's end
    C. birth
    D. death

13. What is one reason an author might choose to write an allegory?
    A. because the writer is interested in detailed descriptions of setting and nuances of character
    B. because the writer is interested in symbolism
    C. because the author thinks that allegories are the most valuable form of literature
    D. because the author is interested in criticizing something indirectly

Reading Skill: Analyzing Cause and Effect *Read the selection. Then, answer the questions that follow.*

Michael stood in the street wondering what to do. It was starting to rain, and he realized that he had left his umbrella at the restaurant during lunch. He quickly ran under a nearby canopy. He wouldn't have forgotten his umbrella if he hadn't been distracted by all the commotion, he thought to himself. Michael had been about to leave the restaurant when a waiter suddenly slipped coming out of the kitchen. When the waiter fell, he dropped a full plate of food onto a customer's lap.

14. What causes Michael to forget his umbrella in the restaurant?
    A. It begins to rain.
    B. He stands under a canopy.
    C. A waiter falls and spills food.
    D. Michael finishes his lunch.

15. What effects are caused by the waiter's fall?
    A. Michael forgets his umbrella.
    B. The waiter drops food on a customer.
    C. Neither a nor b.
    D. Both a and b.

16. What causes Michael to realize that he forgot his umbrella at the restaurant?
    A. It is beginning to rain.
    B. He runs to a nearby canopy.
    C. He remembers the waiter's fall.
    D. He is walking on the street.

17. Which of the following is the definition of the term *cause*?
    A. the result of an action or event
    B. the reason for an action or event
    C. the purpose of a cause or event
    D. the events that occur in a story

18. What is one technique used to analyze cause and effect?
    A. reread
    B. predict what will happen next
    C. visualize the action
    D. analyze character motivation

Reading Strategy: Evaluating Text Format

19. Which of the following are used to format a text?
    A. headings and captions
    B. photographs and illustrations
    C. brochures and advertisements
    D. text and design elements

20. What is a text feature that can help readers evaluate text format?
    A. title page
    B. table of contents
    C. type style and size
    D. headings

Vocabulary: Word Roots

21. What is the meaning of the Latin root contained in the word *verify*?
    A. consequences
    B. truth
    C. explain
    D. verb

22. What is the meaning of the Latin root *-sequi-*?
    A. to explain
    B. to play
    C. to follow
    D. to arrange

23. Using your knowledge of the word root *-sequi-*, what is the meaning of the word *sequential*?
    A. chronological
    B. random
    C. resulting from
    D. once in awhile

Grammar

24. Identify the complete subject and complete predicate of the following sentence.

    Linda read all the available books on the subject.

    A. *Subject:* Linda read   *Predicate:* all the available books on the subject
    B. *Subject:* Linda   *Predicate:* read all the available books on the subject
    C. *Subject:* read all the   *Predicate:* available books on the subject
    D. *Subject:* Linda   *Predicate:* read

25. Which words in the following sentence form the complete predicate?

    At the end of the day, we voted in favor of the committee's recommendation.

    A. at the end of the day
    B. we voted
    C. voted in favor
    D. voted in favor of the committee's recommendation

26. What kind of verb does a plural subject require?
    A. plural
    B. singular
    C. possessive
    D. indefinite

27. Which of the following pronouns may be singular or plural?
    A. everything
    B. anybody
    C. both
    D. none

28. What is the difference between active and passive voice?
    A. A verb in active voice is singular and one in passive voice is plural.
    B. A verb in active voice expresses an action done to its subject, and a verb in passive voice expresses an action done by its subject.
    C. A verb in active voice is interesting, and one in passive voice is boring.
    D. A verb in active voice expresses an action done by its subject, and a verb in passive voice expresses an action done to its subject.

29. What is the best reason to change this sentence to active voice?

    The toys were bought by the twins' mother.

    A. Active voice will make the sentence shorter.
    B. Active voice will make the sentence more direct.
    C. Active voice will draw attention to the sentence.
    D. Active voice is more accurate than passive voice.

30. What is the best reason to use passive voice?
    A. Passive voice is slower paced than active voice.
    B. The performer of the action wants to evade responsibility.
    C. The performer of the action is unknown.
    D. Passive voice is more formal than active voice.

Spelling: Unusual Consonant Groupings

31. This word is spelled incorrectly: *reminice.* Which of the following spellings is correct?
    A. reminise
    B. reminis
    C. reminisce
    D. reminicse

32. This word is spelled incorrectly: *broshure.* Which of the following spellings is correct?
    A. brochure
    B. brochur
    C. broshur
    D. brosure

33. This word is spelled incorrectly: *rithm.* Which of the following spellings is correct?
    A. ruthm
    B. rithem
    C. rhythm
    D. rithim

ESSAY

Writing

34. To help your fellow students, write a column for your school newspaper that offers advice about a topic you know about or a skill or talent that you possess. For example, if you like music, you might want to give advice to students about the elements they can listen for in a piece of music.

35. As a character from a story you read recently, write a letter to a friend describing the events in the story. Use clear descriptions in your writing.

36. Events in nature such as earthquakes, tornadoes, and snowstorms all have distinct causes. The people who live in the areas in which these events occur are affected by these natural events. On a separate piece of paper, write a brief explanation about how people might be affected by a natural event. If time permits, use outside resources to support your explanation.

ANSWERS

"The Jade Peony" by Wayson Choy

Vocabulary Warm-up Exercises, p. 2

A. 1. diagnosed
2. revealed (conveyed)
3. resisted
4. undisturbed
5. elaborate
6. conveyed (revealed)
7. appropriate
8. wondrous

B. Sample Answers

1. *innumerable*: No one could ever count the innumerable grains of sand on the beach.
2. *skillfully*: The outfielder skillfully chased down the ball.
3. *irritation*: The longer I was kept waiting, the more my irritation grew.
4. *pieces*: The vase shattered into a thousand tiny pieces.
5. *puzzled*: The students were puzzled by the confusing assignment.
6. *gloomy*: The funeral was a gloomy occasion.
7. *clearly*: She described the party so clearly that I almost felt as if I had been there.

Reading Warm-up A, p. 3

Sample Answers

1. through a series of grunting noises and elaborate hand gestures; *Conveyed* means "communicated."
2. (shake his head up and down); He might have used his hands to gesture or pantomime.
3. (his complaint); Diseases can also be *diagnosed*.
4. the source of his irritation; Perhaps he was hungry or felt too hot or too cold.
5. by refusing to speak a word of English; Perhaps he only wanted to be helped by the narrator.
6. (his problem); *Appropriate* means "right for the purpose."
7. whatever images flickered across the screen; I enjoy writing poetry when left *undisturbed*.
8. that cranky old man sitting quietly for hours; I beheld the *wondrous* sight of my family having Thanksgiving dinner together with no arguments about football.

Reading Warm-up B, p. 4

Sample Answers

1. There were so many immigrants that it was impossible to count them all; Stars in the sky might be described as *countless*.
2. all the previous generations of their family; My *ancestral* background includes a grandfather who came here from Mexico in the 1950s.

3. (excellent); I can step *deftly* between the new plants in the garden.
4. they realized that their employers had little concern for their comfort or safety; I might feel *exasperation* if I were standing in the rain and my bus was very late.
5. The rock *fragments* were sent flying by the explosions, killing the workers.
6. The mood of the workers; My grandmother's funeral was a *somber* occasion.
7. non-Chinese workers were earning five times as much for their labor; I might be *perplexed* if I showed up at school one day and nobody knew who I was.
8. (long days of backbreaking labor); *Vividly* means "clearly."

Wayson Choy

Listening and Viewing, p. 5

Sample Answers

Segment 1. Choy loved listening to the traditional stories his elders told and wanted to tell his own stories. Students may say that Choy tells stories about his ancestors and his traditional culture so that modern readers can learn about them.

Segment 2. The chimes represent the grandmother and her presence in the family after her death. Students may suggest that a writer uses a symbol to deepen the significance of his or her story.

Segment 3. As one writes, a story becomes stronger: It is re-created through rewriting, and the paper, originally blank, becomes a butterfly when the story is complete. Students may suggest that their writing evolves as they rework it, and in the process, it becomes a complex, finished work.

Segment 4. Wayson Choy believes that literature is important to everyone because it is about all human beings and it can help us understand the past. Students may name books or stories that have taught them something or influenced them or with which they have identified.

Unit 2: Learning About Short Stories, p. 6

1. C; 2. B; 3. C; 4. A; 5. A; 6. C; 7. C; 8. A; 9. B; 10. B

"The Jade Peony" by Wayson Choy

Model Selection: Short Story, p. 7

Sample Answers

1. Grandmama struggles to accept her approaching death and come to terms with the memories of her long-lost love.
2. Sek-Lung struggles with his feelings of fear and loss when he realizes that his beloved grandmother will soon die.
3. The other children struggle with feelings of shame when their grandmother goes through the neighbors' garbage in search of material for her windchimes. They also

struggle to learn Mandarin and pass their examinations. The father apparently struggles to meet deadlines at his job.

4. The setting is a neighborhood in Vancouver, Canada, at a time when tuberculosis was not uncommon.

5. The meeting of two cultures, Chinese and Canadian, is an important aspect of the story. It makes the children feel uneasy—they do not want to appear too "Chinese" to their non-Chinese neighbors, and they question the usefulness of their studying Mandarin. Sek-Lung, however, is fascinated by his Grandmama's stories of her girlhood in China and by her beliefs in signs and spirits. Her conviction that her ghost will return to the family after her death "to say good-bye to this world properly" and that the white cat represents the spirit of her long-lost love are important plot elements.

6. The climax of the story occurs when Grandmama chases the white cat, interprets the cat's appearance as the appearance of her long-lost love's spirit, and believes that it signals that her time has come to die. This is the moment of greatest tension in the story.

7. Love can outweigh death, loss, and suffering. Learning to love is the most valuable lesson that one can learn in life.

Selection Test A, p. 8

Learning About Short Stories

1. ANS: D	DIF: Easy	OBJ: Literary Analysis
2. ANS: C	DIF: Easy	OBJ: Literary Analysis
3. ANS: B	DIF: Easy	OBJ: Literary Analysis
4. ANS: C	DIF: Easy	OBJ: Literary Analysis

Critical Reading

5. ANS: B	DIF: Easy	OBJ: Comprehension
6. ANS: D	DIF: Easy	OBJ: Interpretation
7. ANS: A	DIF: Easy	OBJ: Comprehension
8. ANS: B	DIF: Easy	OBJ: Interpretation
9. ANS: D	DIF: Easy	OBJ: Interpretation
10. ANS: B	DIF: Easy	OBJ: Comprehension
11. ANS: D	DIF: Easy	OBJ: Interpretation
12. ANS: C	DIF: Easy	OBJ: Literary Analysis
13. ANS: C	DIF: Easy	OBJ: Comprehension
14. ANS: C	DIF: Easy	OBJ: Interpretation
15. ANS: C	DIF: Easy	OBJ: Interpretation

Essay

16. Students should realize that the main conflict is Grandmama's coming to terms with—and preparations for—her death. They should recognize that the climax occurs when Grandmama sees the white cat and realizes that her time to die has come. Students will most likely identify the resolution as the grandmother's death and the

narrator's father's act of lifting the windchimes. Alternatively, students may say that the conflict is not resolved because there is no clear indication that the family ever receives the sign that the narrator describes as the story opens, and therefore it is not clear that Grandmama's life has "ended well."

Difficulty: *Easy*

Objective: *Essay*

17. Students may point out that the use of a first-person narrator gives the reader insight into the special bond between Grandmama and Sek-Lung. They might cite, for example, the secret expeditions to find material for the windchimes, Grandmama's recollections of the juggler, and the process of making the windchimes. Students may point out that at the end of the story, the narrator reveals that before she died, Grandmama gave him her Good Fortune pendant. Students should also recognize that the first-person narrator limits the perspective of the story: The reader is not permitted to know a great deal about the thoughts and feelings of the narrator's father, stepmother, and siblings.

Difficulty: *Easy*

Objective: *Essay*

Selection Test B, p. 11

Learning About Short Stories

1. ANS: C	DIF: Average	OBJ: Literary Analysis
2. ANS: D	DIF: Average	OBJ: Literary Analysis
3. ANS: B	DIF: Average	OBJ: Literary Analysis
4. ANS: D	DIF: Average	OBJ: Literary Analysis
5. ANS: B	DIF: Challenging	OBJ: Literary Analysis

Critical Reading

6. ANS: D	DIF: Average	OBJ: Comprehension
7. ANS: C	DIF: Average	OBJ: Interpretation
8. ANS: C	DIF: Challenging	OBJ: Literary Analysis
9. ANS: C	DIF: Average	OBJ: Interpretation
10. ANS: B	DIF: Average	OBJ: Interpretation
11. ANS: C	DIF: Challenging	OBJ: Comprehension
12. ANS: B	DIF: Average	OBJ: Comprehension
13. ANS: C	DIF: Average	OBJ: Comprehension
14. ANS: C	DIF: Average	OBJ: Comprehension
15. ANS: B	DIF: Challenging	OBJ: Comprehension
16. ANS: A	DIF: Average	OBJ: Interpretation
17. ANS: D	DIF: Average	OBJ: Interpretation
18. ANS: C	DIF: Challenging	OBJ: Literary Analysis
19. ANS: D	DIF: Average	OBJ: Interpretation
20. ANS: D	DIF: Average	OBJ: Interpretation

Essay

21. Students should provide one or more examples of at least two of the methods of characterization listed. They may, for example, cite the description of Grandmama's hands. They may quote any of her dialogue—especially her recollections of the juggler, her explanation of the return of her ghost, or her reaction to the white cat—and they might cite her shopping excursions and her method of creating the windchimes. Finally, they may cite her loving relationship with the narrator. Students should conclude their essays with an evaluation of Grandmama's character as a whole.

   Difficulty: *Average*

   Objective: *Essay*

22. Students should identify and discuss some or all of the following conflicts: the family's discomfort with Grandmama's expeditions in search of material for her windchimes; the children's anxiety about studying Mandarin; the narrator's apprehensions about his grandmother's death; Grandmama's struggle to deal with her memories of the juggler, which are symbolized by the jade peony; and Grandmama's struggle to prepare for and accept her death. The conflicts come together and are largely resolved at Grandmama's death, when it is strongly implied that her spirit finds peace. Some students, however, may argue that the conflicts are not resolved, for there is no explicit indication that the sign the family waits for at the beginning of the story ever materializes.

   Difficulty: *Average*

   Objective: *Essay*

23. Students should propose a well-thought-out theme. Some may say that the story is basically about the acceptance of mortality—by both Grandmama and the narrator. Others may focus on the power of love and its connection to artistry and beauty. In that case, they should cite the importance of the jade peony as a symbol of Grandmama's long-lost love for the juggler and of Good Fortune, noting that she passes it on to young Sek-Lung. Students should support their arguments by citing at least two details from the selection.

   Difficulty: *Challenging*

   Objective: *Essay*

Unit 2, Part 1 Answers

Diagnostic Test 3, p. 15

1. ANS: B
2. ANS: C
3. ANS: A
4. ANS: B
5. ANS: A
6. ANS: D
7. ANS: C
8. ANS: D
9. ANS: C
10. ANS: D
11. ANS: B
12. ANS: A
13. ANS: B
14. ANS: D
15. ANS: A

"American History" by Judith Ortiz Cofer

Vocabulary Warm-up Exercises, p. 19

A. 1. paradise
   2. suburbs
   3. impulse
   4. apparent
   5. humiliation
   6. intention
   7. maneuvering
   8. linger

B. Sample Answers

   1. T; *Distraught* means "very upset," and someone who is upset needs comfort.
   2. F; A *version* of you would be someone who is basically like you with only small differences.
   3. T; Handling *rejection* is painful because someone has stopped caring about you.
   4. F; *Anticipated* means that thought was given to something that you expect will occur.
   5. T; *Embrace* means "to give a hug," and we usually hug someone we know well.
   6. F; *Muscular* means "having well-developed muscles," and that is usually a sign of health and good physical condition, not illness.
   7. F; *Smudged* means "messy or unclear," so your paper would be hard to read, not easy.
   8. T; A *temptation* creates a desire to do something wrong or foolish, so it is usually best avoided.

Reading Warm-up A, p. 20

Sample Answers

1. (cities, nearby); No, I live in a small town in the country, and *suburbs* are communities that are located close to cities.
2. call immediately for full independence; *Impulse* is a sudden desire to do something without considering the consequences.
3. (plan); My *intention* is to get my homework done early so I can watch my favorite TV program tonight.
4. clearly understood; They tried to kill U.S. leaders to make it *apparent*, or clear, that they wanted Puerto Rico to be independent from the United States.

5. <u>tried to shoot President Harry Truman and several members of Congress</u>; My *maneuvering* to get invited to the party paid off.

6. (shame); I could not even imagine the *humiliation* the actor felt when he forgot his lines on the opening night of the play.

7. (wealth, happiness); My idea of *paradise* is a place where the sun shines every day.

8. <u>reluctantly leaving</u>; I would *linger* at my friend's house because I really enjoy spending time with her.

Reading Warm-up B, p. 21

Sample Answers

1. (strong); Juan might have become *muscular* from lifting all the heavy boxes of sugar cane.

2. <u>chewing on pieces of the stem to get its delicious, sugary liquid</u>; Yes, I would have had the same *temptation* because I like sweets, even if they are not good for me.

3. With a *smudged* face, Juan would have patches of dirt smeared on his face, which would make him look messy.

4. (thought he would get); Recently, I have *anticipated* the upcoming visit of my cousins.

5. (deeply upset); *Elated* would be an antonym for *distraught* because it means to be very excited and happy, which is the opposite of feeling very upset and distressed.

6. Juan's mother felt *rejection,* or sensed that others did not care about the family, when the people at the bank refused to help by making a loan.

7. <u>With his arms around her</u>; You could be happy or sad because *embrace* means "to give a hug," and people hug in good times and bad.

8. Juan Cheo was strong in body and spirit, and he had the ability to accept what life brings; Yes, I am a *version* of my aunt because she loves to travel and meet new people, and so do I.

"American History" by Judith Ortiz Cofer

Literary Analysis: Conflict, p. 22

Sample Answers

A. 1. Gail and the other African American girls make fun of Elena's Puerto Rican heritage.

2. Elena and Eugene are regarded by their classmates as outsiders and are branded with unflattering nicknames: "Skinny Bones" and "Hick."

3. Elena's mother is concerned about her daughter's behavior with boys. She warns Elena not to become too close to Eugene.

4. Elena struggles to reconcile her feelings for her mother, for the death of President Kennedy, and for Eugene.

5. Elena is hurt when Eugene's mother tells her to go home. Elena realizes that the woman is prejudiced against her because of her ethnic background.

B. The ending does not really resolve the story's multiple conflicts. Instead, it contains an epiphany—a flash of insight in which Elena, the main character, suddenly realizes the realities of racial and ethnic prejudice in the adult world.

Reading: Use Details to Make Inferences, p. 23

Sample Answers

A. 2. Elena feels that the school officials treat non-native speakers of English unfairly.

3. Elena's mother is worried about her daughter's behavior around boys. She does not seem to trust Elena.

4. Elena's mother is shocked at Elena's lack of concern for the assassinated president.

5. Eugene's mother is prejudiced against the Puerto Ricans who live in El Building.

6. Elena feels sad and disillusioned because of her rejection by Eugene's mother.

Sample Answer

B. Elena has grown up because she has come to realize that many groups, including her own family and fellow Puerto Rican immigrants, are forced to confront prejudice and discrimination. She has also grown up because she realizes that her relationship with Eugene was built largely on fantasy.

Vocabulary Builder, p. 24

Sample Answers

A. 1. A tenement looks run-down.

2. She is deeply worried about the move.

3. I feel that I can trust her.

4. The watchdog is doing its job well.

5. No. A dilapidated house is in very poor condition and needs many repairs.

B. 1. As Elena stared at the dilapidated tenement, she felt a profound disillusionment.

2. The building's security guard was discreet, but we knew that he was continually vigilant, on the watch for intruders.

Enrichment: History of Puerto Rico, p. 27

Sample Answers

1. Puerto Rico was a Spanish colony for more than 350 years.

2. At the end of the Spanish-American War, the Treaty of Paris (December 10, 1898) made Puerto Rico a U.S. possession.

3. Citizens of Puerto Rico are U.S. citizens.

4. A commonwealth is a self-governing part of the United States. It is not a state, however.

Selection Test A, p. 28

Critical Reading

1. ANS: C   DIF: Easy   OBJ: Comprehension
2. ANS: C   DIF: Easy   OBJ: Reading
3. ANS: B   DIF: Easy   OBJ: Interpretation
4. ANS: D   DIF: Easy   OBJ: Reading
5. ANS: D   DIF: Easy   OBJ: Literary Analysis
6. ANS: C   DIF: Easy   OBJ: Comprehension
7. ANS: C   DIF: Easy   OBJ: Comprehension
8. ANS: C   DIF: Easy   OBJ: Interpretation
9. ANS: C   DIF: Easy   OBJ: Reading
10. ANS: A   DIF: Easy   OBJ: Comprehension
11. ANS: D   DIF: Easy   OBJ: Interpretation
12. ANS: C   DIF: Easy   OBJ: Literary Analysis

Vocabulary and Grammar

13. ANS: A   DIF: Easy   OBJ: Vocabulary
14. ANS: C   DIF: Easy   OBJ: Grammar
15. ANS: A   DIF: Easy   OBJ: Grammar

Essay

16. Students may identify any two conflicts. External conflicts: Elena vs. Gail and the other students; Elena vs. the school, which excludes her from honors classes; Elena vs. her mother; and Elena vs. Eugene's mother. Students may also identify Elena's internal conflict concerning how she should behave on the day of President Kennedy's assassination. The conflicts remain unresolved. Elena experiences an epiphany when she realizes that Eugene's mother is prejudiced against her. She realizes that her dreams of friendship with Eugene that she had cherished are futile.
    Difficulty: *Easy*
    Objective: *Essay*

17. Students should point out that the story's title has multiple meanings. American History is the subject that Eugene has invited Elena to study with him. More broadly, the story is set on a notable day in American history: November 22, 1963, the day on which President Kennedy was assassinated in Dallas, Texas. Finally, the title may hint at the social message of the story: that prejudice against different races and ethnic groups is a continuing theme in American history.
    Difficulty: *Easy*
    Objective: *Essay*

Selection Test B, p. 31

Critical Reading

1. ANS: D   DIF: Average   OBJ: Comprehension
2. ANS: C   DIF: Average   OBJ: Comprehension
3. ANS: C   DIF: Challenging   OBJ: Reading

4. ANS: B   DIF: Average   OBJ: Interpretation
5. ANS: B   DIF: Average   OBJ: Literary Analysis
6. ANS: B   DIF: Challenging   OBJ: Interpretation
7. ANS: D   DIF: Average   OBJ: Reading
8. ANS: B   DIF: Challenging   OBJ: Interpretation
9. ANS: D   DIF: Average   OBJ: Literary Analysis
10. ANS: C   DIF: Average   OBJ: Comprehension
11. ANS: C   DIF: Average   OBJ: Reading
12. ANS: A   DIF: Average   OBJ: Comprehension
13. ANS: B   DIF: Challenging   OBJ: Literary Analysis
14. ANS: D   DIF: Average   OBJ: Interpretation

Vocabulary and Grammar

15. ANS: A   DIF: Average   OBJ: Vocabulary
16. ANS: C   DIF: Challenging   OBJ: Vocabulary
17. ANS: B   DIF: Average   OBJ: Vocabulary
18. ANS: C   DIF: Average   OBJ: Grammar
19. ANS: C   DIF: Average   OBJ: Grammar
20. ANS: A   DIF: Average   OBJ: Grammar

Essay

21. Students may identify any three conflicts. External conflicts include the following: Elena vs. Gail and other students who mock her at school; Elena vs. the school authorities who exclude her from honors classes; Elena vs. her mother, who warns Elena about her feelings for Eugene and then wants her daughter to accompany her to church on the day of the assassination; Elena vs. Eugene's mother, who sharply rebuffs her when she arrives to study with Eugene. Elena's internal conflicts include the following: her struggle to honor President Kennedy vs. her elation at Eugene's invitation, her feelings of turbulence as she dreams about growing up and becoming an adult, and her sadness at her rejection by Eugene's mother. Students should note that none of these conflicts are resolved. However, Elena does experience an epiphany when she is turned away by Eugene's mother. She realizes that Eugene's family does not accept her and that her dreams of friendship with Eugene are futile.
    Difficulty: *Average*
    Objective: *Essay*

22. Students should point out that El Building, the center for newly arrived Puerto Rican immigrants in the narrator's town of Paterson, New Jersey, has a strong presence in the story. The dilapidated apartment building is usually full of life; on the other hand, on the day of the Kennedy assassination, it is eerily quiet. Elena's mother feels unhappy in El Building, and the family dreams of moving so that they can own their own home. Elena notices that El Building blocks most of the sun, and the only place nearby that gets any sunlight is the tiny area of Eugene's

yard. On the whole, El Building establishes a mood of conflict and claustrophobia. Just as Elena's family is eager to move, Elena herself feels trapped by unhappiness and frustration for much of the story.

Difficulty: *Average*

Objective: *Essay*

"The Most Dangerous Game" by Richard Connell

Vocabulary Warm-up Exercises, p. 35

A. 1. bewilderment
2. acknowledge
3. particularly
4. complicated
5. vivid
6. consideration
7. superstition
8. grisly

B. Sample Answers

1. F; Greeting someone *enthusiastically* would be acting in an excited, positive way, so your friend would be glad to see you, not unhappy.
2. T; You might be worried that you will do badly on a hard test.
3. T; A *jagged* road would be uneven, with many sharp turns that would require skillful driving.
4. F; *Postponing* means "delaying until later," so you will be traveling eventually.
5. F; An *inspiration* is a sudden good idea and is something you are more likely to get when you are awake.
6. F; A *trait* is a feature that makes someone or something stand out and should be apparent to anyone who pays attention.
7. T; Overcoming an *obstacle* means getting around something in the way, and it usually takes strength or determination, which are qualities that people admire.
8. T; *Precision* means "accuracy," and an engineer who builds something and a surgeon who operates on people both need to be very accurate in their work.

Reading Warm-up A, p. 36

Sample Answers

1. (sport); Some people view hunting as *grisly* because they do not approve of killing animals.
2. extreme accuracy; *Vague* or *unclear* would be an antonym for *vivid* in the passage.
3. deep confusion; Yes, a new student might feel *bewilderment* because everything is new. He or she would not know his or her way around or even know whom to ask for help.
4. (true); He created many national parks and preserves.

5. Roosevelt's views on hunting; *Simple* is an antonym for *complicated*.
6. (bad omens); A common *superstition* is believing that walking under a ladder will bring bad luck.
7. to a degree not seen after him; It is *particularly* easy for me to make friends because I like people and get along with others.
8. (kindness); Students could show more *consideration* at school by being more polite to teachers and to other students.

Reading Warm-up B, p. 37

Sample Answers

1. With the vast ocean all around, he was forever picking up objects that he could use for some purpose or that triggered amazing tales in his mind of their journeys across the sea. Yes, I had an *inspiration* to paint my room after watching a home makeover show on television.
2. (block); Speaking a different language might be a learning *obstacle*. To get around it, the student would need to learn English.
3. (waiting); No, they are not the same because *canceling* means something is not happening at all. *Postponing* means putting something off to a later time or date.
4. razor-sharp stones; *Smooth* is an antonym for *jagged*.
5. She always worried that something might happen to her children; *Relaxed* is an antonym for *apprehensive*.
6. *Characteristic* is a synonym for *trait*. A *trait* that distinguishes me is loyalty because I always stick by my friends.
7. (eager); Someone who is behaving *enthusiastically* would be very excited.
8. careful; exact; *Accuracy* is a synonym for *precision*, and *sloppy* is an adjective that means the opposite.

"The Most Dangerous Game" by Richard Connell

Literary Analysis: Conflict, p. 38

Sample Answers

A. 1. Rainsford battles the ocean and the rough surf as he swims to the island. He also battles the jungle when he is being hunted by Zaroff.
2. Zaroff forces his visitors to play the role of quarry for him. Without exception, he corners and kills each visitor.
3. Rainsford squares off against Zaroff in a deadly battle of wits and hunting skills. If Zaroff succeeds, he will kill Rainsford.
4. Rainsford must struggle to remain calm and keep his wits about him.

B. The story's ending resolves the main conflict. Rainsford defeats Zaroff, kills him, and sleeps in the general's bed. Whether Rainsford's experience has changed his attitude toward big-game hunting is debatable. The most one can say is that now he knows how it feels to be the "huntee."

Reading: Use Details to Make Inferences, p. 39
Sample Answers
A. 2. Rainsford is frightened. He is disgusted by Zaroff.
   3. Zaroff cares more about the death of a dog than about the death of a human being.
   4. Rainsford's hunting experience makes him a worthy opponent. Rainsford is able to remain calm and resourceful.
B. Most students will say that the story serves as an entertaining tale and that there is no serious theme, or message about human life or behavior. However, if students identify a theme, be sure that they use details and examples from the text to support their interpretation.

Vocabulary Builder, p. 40
Sample Answers
A. 1. If you are too slow in starting, you may not finish by the time that the paper is due.
   2. Your conscience is bothering you. You are having doubts that what you are about to do is right.
   3. You would feel disappointed and upset.
   4. A naive person believes everything you say and never suspects he or she is being fooled.
   5. Yes; the fans are feeling suspense.
B. 1. His sense of guilt was palpable as he told us of his efforts to ignore his scruples while cheating on the test.
   2. Because she approaches every task indolently, she was unprepared for the job interview, which made it a futile exercise.
   3. Do you think a naive person is likely to have scruples about sneaking into a movie?

Enrichment: Dealing With Competition, p. 43
Sample Answers
1. Jose could invite other children over to play team basketball instead of playing one-on-one versus his brother.
2. The club can choose different teams for every game and not keep standings.
3. Solos could be awarded on a rotating basis, not through tryouts.
4. Students can speak with the teacher first. Then, they might meet with the student and tell him or her how they feel.
5. You could sit down with your friend and discuss your concerns about your working relationship.

"American History" by Judith Ortiz Cofer
"The Most Dangerous Game" by Richard Connell

Build Language Skills: Vocabulary, p. 44
Sample Answers
A. 1. to think about
   She spent all afternoon speculating about her chances for promotion at the office.
   2. ghost
   People claim to have seen the specter of a weeping woman in that old house.
   3. roundabout, indirect way of expressing something
   She replied with lengthy circumlocutions instead of a direct answer.
   4. to limit
   The new law drastically circumscribes that agency's authority.
B. 1. Appeals to emotion usually involve the heart more than the head.
   2. Characters might be categorized as major or minor or as dynamic or static.
   3. Writers use the element of setting to describe the circumstances of a story.
   4. A character's thoughts, words, and actions often reveal his or her motives.
   5. Point of view is an important aspect because it controls what the reader knows in a story.

Build Language Skills: Grammar, p. 45
A. 1. *walk*: walking, walked, (has) walked
   hunt: hunting, hunted, (has) hunted
   place: placing, placed, (has) placed
   rip: ripping, ripped, (has) ripped
   2. *-ed* or *-d*
B. 1. *Correct*
   2. After school started, Elena looked for Eugene in all her classes.
   3. Mr. DePalma has asked us to line up in front of him.
   4. Rainsford was exhausted when he arrived on the island.

"The Most Dangerous Game" by Richard Connell

Selection Test A, p. 46
Critical Reading

1. ANS: C	DIF: Easy	OBJ: Interpretation
2. ANS: C	DIF: Easy	OBJ: Interpretation
3. ANS: B	DIF: Easy	OBJ: Comprehension
4. ANS: A	DIF: Easy	OBJ: Literary Analysis

5. ANS: C	DIF: Easy	OBJ: Interpretation
6. ANS: D	DIF: Easy	OBJ: Interpretation
7. ANS: C	DIF: Easy	OBJ: Reading
8. ANS: B	DIF: Easy	OBJ: Reading
9. ANS: A	DIF: Easy	OBJ: Literary Analysis
10. ANS: D	DIF: Easy	OBJ: Literary Analysis
11. ANS: A	DIF: Easy	OBJ: Literary Analysis

Vocabulary and Grammar

12. ANS: C	DIF: Easy	OBJ: Vocabulary
13. ANS: B	DIF: Easy	OBJ: Vocabulary
14. ANS: D	DIF: Easy	OBJ: Grammar
15. ANS: C	DIF: Easy	OBJ: Grammar

Essay

16. Students may say that Rainsford is concerned about his safety, he is sickened by Zaroff's game, he questions Zaroff's sanity, and he thinks about escape. Rainsford thinks that Zaroff is a murderer, and he becomes ill after learning about Zaroff's game. He desperately considers how to escape from his predicament.

Difficulty: *Easy*

Objective: *Essay*

17. Students should point out that, at the beginning of the story, Rainsford thinks hunting is "the best sport in the world." He does not care how the jaguar feels; he thinks there are two classes: "the hunters and the huntees." By the end, Rainsford knows how an animal feels when it is being hunted.

Difficulty: *Easy*

Objective: *Essay*

Selection Test B, p. 49

Critical Reading

1. ANS: C	DIF: Average	OBJ: Interpretation
2. ANS: C	DIF: Challenging	OBJ: Interpretation
3. ANS: B	DIF: Challenging	OBJ: Reading Strategy
4. ANS: C	DIF: Average	OBJ: Comprehension
5. ANS: D	DIF: Average	OBJ: Interpretation
6. ANS: A	DIF: Average	OBJ: Literary Analysis
7. ANS: C	DIF: Average	OBJ: Reading Strategy
8. ANS: A	DIF: Average	OBJ: Literary Analysis
9. ANS: D	DIF: Average	OBJ: Literary Analysis
10. ANS: A	DIF: Average	OBJ: Reading Strategy
11. ANS: A	DIF: Average	OBJ: Literary Analysis
12. ANS: C	DIF: Average	OBJ: Interpretation
13. ANS: D	DIF: Challenging	OBJ: Interpretation

Vocabulary and Grammar

14. ANS: C	DIF: Challenging	OBJ: Vocabulary
15. ANS: B	DIF: Average	OBJ: Vocabulary
16. ANS: D	DIF: Average	OBJ: Grammar
17. ANS: D	DIF: Average	OBJ: Vocabulary
18. ANS: B	DIF: Average	OBJ: Grammar
19. ANS: C	DIF: Average	OBJ: Grammar

Essay

20. Students may point out that, while the statement may be an apt metaphor for the human condition, it becomes a gruesome joke if taken literally. They should point out that Rainsford, through his desperate battle with the general, gains a better perspective on what it feels like to be the huntee.

Difficulty: *Average*

Objective: *Essay*

21. Students should include such similarities between the two men as the following: both are intelligent, cunning, physically fit, and familiar with a number of hunting tricks. In addition, both men are worldly and sophisticated. As a contrast, students should point out that Zaroff has lost all sense of moral balance.

Difficulty: *Average*

Objective: *Essay*

22. Students should include some of the following suspenseful episodes: Rainsford's falling overboard and his struggle to reach land, his being held at gunpoint by Ivan, his sudden realization of Zaroff's intentions, his first anxious evening in the jungle, his traps, and Zaroff's narrow escapes. Students should note that the author's suspenseful tone and precise descriptions help convey the desperation of Rainsford and make the reader wish to continue reading to find out what happens.

Difficulty: *Challenging*

Objective: *Essay*

"The Gift of the Magi" by O. Henry

Vocabulary Warm-up Exercises, p. 53

A. 1. hysterical
2. metaphor
3. rippling
4. calculated
5. immediate
6. sacrificed
7. craved
8. privilege

B. Sample Answers

1. F; *Adorned* means to "decorated," so the room would be less plain.
2. F; *Generosity* is the willingness to give, and people can give things like time and love that do not involve money.
3. T; *Inconsequential* means "not important," so worrying about something that does not matter is not wise.
4. F; *Agile* means "quick and flexible," not "awkward."
5. T; *Scrutiny* means "close examination," and a used car might have problems you would want to know about before you buy it.
6. F; *Prosperity* means "wealth or success," and a ragged appearance would more likely show poverty or failure.
7. T; *Sentiments* are feelings that influence what we think.
8. F; *Sequence* means "order," so one event must follow the other.

Reading Warm-up A, p. 54

Sample Answers

1. Gilded Age; an America that glittered with the wealth of a few.
2. counting pennies; giving up long hours to hard work.
3. great profits could be made with a new kind of store; The businessmen *calculated* that they could make a lot of money if people could find everything they needed in one store.
4. (advantage); I have the *privilege* of being the oldest child in my family, which means I get to control the TV remote.
5. (Almost instantly); A store that was an *immediate* success would be filled with shoppers from the day it opened and would be making money right away.
6. (waves of customers); In this passage, *rippling* means they were always on the move, a constant wave of shoppers on the streets.
7. desperately wanted; *Avoided* or *shunned* would be the opposite of *craved*.
8. uncontrolled excitement; *Hysterical* shoppers might be grabbing at things and fighting with others over merchandise.

Reading Warm-up B, p. 55

Sample Answers

1. used to enhance beauty, flowers, gold ornaments; *Adorned* means "decorated or made more attractive."
2. (important); I consider appearance to be *inconsequential* because what really matters is who you are as a person.
3. blond hair was better than their own dark hair; I use *sentiments* to describe opinions because the word conveys that feelings and a point of view are involved.
4. one following the other; Folowing the *sequence* of events of my day, I go to school during the day, I have sports

practice in the afternoon, then I go home for dinner, and in the evening I watch television and do my homework.

5. (wealthy); *Poverty* or *failure* are antonyms for *prosperity*.
6. *Inspection* is a synonym for *scrutiny*; No, I would not feel comfortable because it would mean that I was being watched carefully, which might imply that someone thinks I have done something wrong.
7. move easily; Yes, it would be a compliment because someone who is *agile* is quick and usually graceful, and those are positive qualities.
8. people donate their hair for wigs that go to children with cancer; I could show *generosity* by giving my time to a good cause.

"The Gift of the Magi" by O. Henry

Literary Analysis: Irony and Surprise Ending, p. 56

Sample Answers

A.
1. I; We might have expected that she would have been able to save more over such a long period.
2. I; The woman's elegant-sounding name makes us expect someone beautiful and sophisticated, but she is not.
3. N; This is simple description; nothing indicates reversal.
4. I; The combs are meant to decorate Della's beautiful hair, but she has sold her hair to buy Jim's gift.

B. Both Jim and Della sell their most treasured possessions (Jim sells his watch and Della sells her hair) to buy each other a special Christmas present. Ironically, the presents they buy turn out to be useless because they no longer possess the items they have sold. O. Henry makes the surprise ending seem logical because he shows us Della's and Jim's deep love for each other and their capacity for sacrifice. He also identifies the couple's prized possessions early in the story.

Reading: Use Prior Knowledge and Experience to Make Inferences, p. 57

Sample Answers

A.

Della
2. *(Details/Inferences)* She scarcely hesitates before she sells her hair. / She is impulsive but also generous.
3. *(Details/Inferences)* She spends a lot of time choosing the right present for Jim. / She knows her husband's character and wants to please him.

Jim
2. *(Details/Inferences)* He is never late. / He is organized and conscientious.
3. *(Details/Inferences)* He needs a new overcoat and has no gloves. / He does not spend much money on himself.

Vocabulary Builder, p. 58

A. 1. discreet 2. instigates 3. depreciate

B. 1. F; Someone who instigates conflict causes—not solves—problems.

2. T; The value of a car will be reduced after 6 years of hard use.

3. T; Someone who is discreet will keep a secret.

C. 1. A; 2. C; 3. D

Enrichment: Calculating Inflation, p. 61

1. 2006 cost: $100; $100 −$30 = $70 price increase; 70 ÷ 30 = 2.33 = <u>233% inflation over 100 years</u>; 2.33 ÷ 100 years = .023 = <u>2.3% inflation per year</u>

2. 2006 cost: $3.59; $3.59 ÷ $ .18 = $3.41 price increase; 3.41 ÷ $ .18 = 18.94 = <u>1894% inflation over 100 years</u>; 18.94 ÷ 100 years = .1894 = <u>18.94% inflation per year</u>

3. 2006 cost: $ .37; $ .37 −$ .02 = $ .35 price increase; .35 ÷ .02 = 17.5 = <u>1750% inflation over 100 years</u>; 17.50 ÷ 100 years = .175 = <u>17.5% inflation per year</u>

4. 2006 cost: $10.50; $10.50 −$ .05 = $10.45 price increase; 10.45 ÷ $ .05 = 209 = <u>20,900% inflation over 100 years</u>; 209 ÷ 100 years = 2.09 = <u>209% inflation per year</u>

5. 2006 cost: $19,000; $19,000 −$500 = $18,500 price increase; 18,500 ÷ 500 = 37.00 = <u>3700% inflation over 100 years</u>; 37 ÷ 100 years = .37 = <u>37% inflation per year</u>

Selection Test A, p. 62

Critical Reading

1. ANS: D	DIF: Easy	OBJ: Comprehension
2. ANS: A	DIF: Easy	OBJ: Comprehension
3. ANS: B	DIF: Easy	OBJ: Reading
4. ANS: A	DIF: Easy	OBJ: Interpretation
5. ANS: B	DIF: Easy	OBJ: Reading
6. ANS: B	DIF: Easy	OBJ: Literary Analysis
7. ANS: A	DIF: Easy	OBJ: Reading
8. ANS: C	DIF: Easy	OBJ: Comprehension
9. ANS: D	DIF: Easy	OBJ: Interpretation
10. ANS: B	DIF: Easy	OBJ: Literary Analysis
11. ANS: A	DIF: Easy	OBJ: Interpretation

Vocabulary and Grammar

12. ANS: C	DIF: Easy	OBJ: Vocabulary
13. ANS: B	DIF: Easy	OBJ: Vocabulary
14. ANS: C	DIF: Easy	OBJ: Grammar
15. ANS: D	DIF: Easy	OBJ: Grammar

Essay

16. Students should point out that Jim and Della are foolish in their sacrifices, selling their most treasured posses-sions. Yet at the same time, they are wise because their sacrifices show the depth and value of their love for each other.

Difficulty: *Easy*

Objective: *Essay*

17. Students should point out that the irony in the story's plot is closely linked to Jim's and Della's decisions to sacrifice their prized possessions. Ironically, each gift the couple buys is closely related to the items they sell. Students may comment that the surprise ending leaves them with feelings of sympathy and admiration for the couple. These feelings are related to the story's message that the best gifts are those given out of love.

Difficulty: *Easy*

Objective: *Essay*

Selection Test B, p. 65

Critical Reading

1. ANS: D	DIF: Average	OBJ: Comprehension
2. ANS: B	DIF: Average	OBJ: Comprehension
3. ANS: D	DIF: Average	OBJ: Interpretation
4. ANS: B	DIF: Average	OBJ: Reading Strategy
5. ANS: A	DIF: Average	OBJ: Interpretation
6. ANS: B	DIF: Challenging	OBJ: Reading
7. ANS: B	DIF: Average	OBJ: Literary Analysis
8. ANS: A	DIF: Average	OBJ: Reading
9. ANS: C	DIF: Average	OBJ: Reading
10. ANS: B	DIF: Challenging	OBJ: Literary Analysis
11. ANS: D	DIF: Average	OBJ: Interpretation
12. ANS: B	DIF: Challenging	OBJ: Literary Analysis
13. ANS: A	DIF: Average	OBJ: Interpretation

Vocabulary and Grammar

14. ANS: C	DIF: Average	OBJ: Vocabulary
15. ANS: C	DIF: Challenging	OBJ: Vocabulary
16. ANS: D	DIF: Average	OBJ: Vocabulary
17. ANS: C	DIF: Average	OBJ: Grammar
18. ANS: B	DIF: Challenging	OBJ: Grammar

Essay

19. Students should note that the following details describe an impoverished living situation: the "shabby little couch," the empty letter box, and the broken electric doorbell. Students may also note that Della counts her $1.87 three times, indicating that Jim and Della are struggling to make ends meet. Students can infer that these young people are hard-working, determined, con-scientious, and deeply in love.

Difficulty: *Average*

Objective: *Essay*

20. Students should point out that the ironic twists in the story's plot are closely linked to the determination of Jim and Della to make a significant sacrifice to buy each other a special gift. This sacrifice involves giving up their dearest possessions: the watch and the hair. Ironically, however, each gift is closely related to the items the couple sells. Thus, the fob and chain are useless without Jim's watch, and the combs are useless without Della's hair. Students may comment that the surprise ending leaves them with feelings of sympathy and admiration for the young couple's devotion to each other. These emotions, in turn, are related to the story's theme: The best gifts are those made out of love.

Difficulty: *Average*

Objective: *Essay*

21. Most students will state that Jim and Della are foolish to sell their watch and hair—their greatest treasures—for expensive gifts that they cannot otherwise afford. Some students may note that more practical gift choices would have been a warm coat or gloves for the winter season. However, in their foolishness, Jim and Della demonstrate their wise instinct to sacrifice what is dearest to them in order to give a special present to the other. Students may say that they are foolish in their choices but wise in their love for each other.

Difficulty: *Challenging*

Objective: *Essay*

"The Interlopers" by Saki

Vocabulary Warm-up Exercises, p. 69

A. 1. relationships
2. evident
3. disputed
4. boundary
5. harbored
6. assuredly
7. restless
8. dramatic

B. Sample Answers
1. F; When you *compromised*, you gave up part of what you wanted.
2. F; A *lawsuit* is a legal case that is settled in a courtroom.
3. F; If views are *distinctly* different, the differences should be clear to see.
4. T; A person on the *outlook* for a storm would watch the sky for dark clouds.
5. F; *Passions* involve strong emotional responses, so the person is more likely to be involved than bored.
6. F; A *territorial* problem would be of interest mainly to people in a specific area.
7. T; A driver who is *unstrung* might be distracted on the road.

8. F; *Violence* involves physical confrontation, which is a poor way to resolve problems.

Reading Warm-up A, p. 70

Sample Answers
1. that some problems are harder to deal with than others; *Certainly* is a synonym for *assuredly*.
2. each side claims as its own; I remember the *disputed* grade on that difficult essay test I took last year.
3. (border); The Rio Grande forms the *boundary* between Texas and Mexico.
4. (minerals); *Harbored* means "was a home to."
5. spouses, brothers and sisters, or parents and children; My mother and my aunt and my twin brothers have extremely close *relationships*.
6. (resentment, anger); It could be *dramatic* if the person started yelling or crying.
7. hiding one's true feelings is not a good way to resolve conflicts; *Evident* means "easily noticed or understood."
8. (impatient); Having to sit still during a boring concert makes me *restless*.

Reading Warm-up B, p. 71

Sample Answers
1. (courts); Arthur plans to file a lawsuit because Jacob has not paid his rent for almost six months.
2. telling him that his rent is due on the first day of every month; I can *distinctly* recall telling my brother not to borrow my baseball glove.
3. as if he wanted to hit me; I might become *unstrung* if I had to go to my little sister's dance recital when I was planning to go to my friend's party.
4. I am on the *outlook* every day for an opportunity to practice my dancing.
5. *Violence*, or force, might be justified if someone were being physically attacked and there was no other way to stop the attacker.
6. by offering to let him pay me half the money now and the balance of his debt in monthly installments; *Compromised* means "settled only when both sides give up something."
7. Jacob implied that the property did not really belong to Arthur, or that Arthur had no *territorial* rights to it.
8. (emotional); Jacob could not talk rationally because *passions* are strong emotions that can affect the way a person thinks.

"The Interlopers" by Saki

Literary Analysis: Irony and Surprise Ending, p. 72

Sample Answers
A. 1. I; Expectations are reversed when Ulrich suddenly gets his wish.

2. N; This sentence simply describes a shift in the men's behavior.

3. I; Earlier, each man prayed that his followers would arrive first so that he could destroy his enemy. Now, both men pray that their followers might arrive first so that they might display friendship and honor.

4. N; This sentence is simply descriptive.

B. Students should point out that the two men had expected their followers to catch up with them eventually and come to their rescue. Instead, Ulrich realizes at the end of the story that they are being hunted by wolves. Saki makes the ending seem logical by emphasizing the wildness, loneliness, and danger of the setting. Also, the wolves' presumed hostility toward the men echoes the men's bitter hatred for each other at the beginning of the story.

Reading: Use Prior Knowledge and Experience to Make Inferences, p. 73

Sample Answers

A.

Ulrich

2. He offers Georg a drink from the wine flask. / He is capable of human sympathy.

3. He calls Georg "neighbor." / He is tired of the old feud and thinks it is futile.

Georg

2. He continues to trespass on the disputed land. / He believes his own "rights" are superior to the court's decision.

3. He taunts Ulrich for being caught fast in his "stolen forest." / Even when he is caught in a desperate situation, he is capable of mocking his enemy.

Vocabulary Builder, p. 74

A. 1. languor 2. condolences 3. precipitous

B. Sample Answers

1. I sent my <u>condolences</u> when I heard of her grandfather's death.

2. We had a difficult three-mile hike over a rocky, <u>precipitous</u> trail.

3. She arises every morning filled with <u>languor</u>, reluctant to leave her bed.

C. 1. A; 2. C; 3. B

Enrichment: Problem Solving, p. 77

Sample Answers

3. The two families can meet separately to discuss the end of the feud. Then, they can form a committee to create guidelines for using the land and another committee to plan regular social functions between the families.

4. The committees might meet for regular sessions to discuss any issues and unexpected problems that arise.

5. The committees can change rules or decide to eliminate rules that are no longer needed.

"The Gift of the Magi" by O. Henry
"The Interlopers" by Saki

Build Language Skills: Vocabulary, p. 78

Sample Answers

A. 1. distant; faraway

Patagonia strikes most visitors as remote and exotic.

2. feeling

I never reread "The Gift of the Magi" without being overcome by emotion.

3. turbulence; confusion

When the flight was canceled, there was a lot of commotion among the passengers.

4. advancement in rank or position

Maria was thrilled with her promotion as the new head of information services.

B. 1. The lead editorial made several appeals to readers' *emotion* of civic pride.

2. In that detective novel, the murderer's *motive* is jealousy.

3. The jury asked for more details about the *circumstances* of the crime.

4. Biologists have *categorized* wild tigers into eight subspecies.

5. One *aspect* of the film that especially impressed me was the special effects.

Build Language Skills: Grammar, p. 79

A. 1. sold; 2. run; 3. began

B. 1. Although Saki wrote history, novels, and political satire, he is known especially for his short stories.

2. Born in Burma as H. H. Munro, he was brought up in England by two aunts.

3. As a foreign correspondent, he spent time in Poland, Russia, and Paris.

"The Interlopers" by Saki

Selection Test A, p. 80

Critical Reading

1. ANS: A	DIF: Easy	OBJ: Interpretation
2. ANS: A	DIF: Easy	OBJ: Interpretation
3. ANS: D	DIF: Easy	OBJ: Reading
4. ANS: C	DIF: Easy	OBJ: Comprehension

5. ANS: C	DIF: Easy	OBJ: Literary Analysis
6. ANS: D	DIF: Easy	OBJ: Reading
7. ANS: D	DIF: Easy	OBJ: Comprehension
8. ANS: C	DIF: Easy	OBJ: Literary Analysis
9. ANS: C	DIF: Easy	OBJ: Literary Analysis
10. ANS: B	DIF: Easy	OBJ: Interpretation
11. ANS: B	DIF: Easy	OBJ: Interpretation

Vocabulary and Grammar

12. ANS: B	DIF: Easy	OBJ: Vocabulary
13. ANS: D	DIF: Easy	OBJ: Vocabulary
14. ANS: C	DIF: Easy	OBJ: Grammar
15. ANS: A	DIF: Easy	OBJ: Grammar

Essay

16. Students should realize that what makes the ending of the story surprising is that the figures in the woods are not what they appear to be. The men have been calling for help, and they know that their own friends are not too far away. When they call for help and see figures approaching, the reader, like the characters, assumes that the figures are their friends. When it becomes clear that the figures are wolves, the reader is surprised and horrified by the men's situation.

Difficulty: *Easy*
Objective: *Essay*

17. Students should point out that "Nature's own violence" first overwhelms the men when a tree falls on them and again when wolves stalk them as they lie trapped beneath the tree. Students should point out the author's message: The natural world is indifferent to the petty fights, grand plans, and wishes of humans.

Difficulty: *Easy*
Objective: *Essay*

Selection Test B, p. 83

Critical Reading

1. ANS: A	DIF: Average	OBJ: Interpretation
2. ANS: D	DIF: Average	OBJ: Reading
3. ANS: C	DIF: Average	OBJ: Comprehension
4. ANS: C	DIF: Average	OBJ: Reading
5. ANS: D	DIF: Challenging	OBJ: Literary Analysis
6. ANS: A	DIF: Challenging	OBJ: Literary Analysis
7. ANS: D	DIF: Average	OBJ: Comprehension
8. ANS: B	DIF: Average	OBJ: Interpretation
9. ANS: C	DIF: Average	OBJ: Literary Analysis
10. ANS: C	DIF: Average	OBJ: Literary Analysis
11. ANS: D	DIF: Challenging	OBJ: Interpretation
12. ANS: B	DIF: Average	OBJ: Interpretation

Vocabulary and Grammar

13. ANS: A	DIF: Average	OBJ: Vocabulary
14. ANS: D	DIF: Average	OBJ: Vocabulary
15. ANS: C	DIF: Average	OBJ: Grammar
16. ANS: C	DIF: Average	OBJ: Grammar
17. ANS: A	DIF: Average	OBJ: Grammar

Essay

18. Students should note that the life-threatening situation puts the feud into perspective for the men. Their bitter land dispute seems unimportant. Ironically, it has taken them a long time to consider exchanging friendship for bitter hostility. The changes probably occur because Georg and Ulrich are frightened and lonely and have no choice but to talk and listen to each other. At the end of the story, in a further ironic twist, the men learn that the figures that are moving toward them are wolves instead of rescuers. The reader realizes that if the wolves attack and kill the men, their change of heart will have come about much too late to have any practical effect.

Difficulty: *Average*
Objective: *Essay*

19. Students should point out that "Nature's own violence" first overwhelms the men when a tree falls on them and again when wolves stalk them as they lie trapped beneath the tree. Students should point out that the author intends to show the indifference of the natural world to the petty fights, grand plans, and wishes of human beings. Students may note that the author conveys the message that people's grand schemes and wishes are insignificant if they are in conflict with the natural world.

Difficulty: *Average*
Objective: *Essay*

20. Students should explain that the word *interlopers* can apply to Georg and his followers, who trespass and hunt on Ulrich's land. A second interpretation is that Ulrich and Georg, who have feuded bitterly over a narrow strip of land, may be regarded as foolish intruders in a natural world that they can never truly "own" or control. Finally, the wolves turn out to be the intruders on Ulrich and Georg's plans, grimly stalking the men as the story concludes.

Difficulty: *Challenging*
Objective: *Essay*

"The Man to Send Rain Clouds"
by Leslie Marmon Silko
"Old Man of the Temple" by R. K. Narayan

Vocabulary Warm-up Exercises, p. 87

A. 1. ceremonial
2. ensure

3. cheekbones
4. scuffed
5. wilted
6. penetrated
7. glossy
8. sundown

B. Sample Answers

1. You should go to a doctor or an emergency room because *continuous* pain never stops. Not only would you be uncomfortable, but there could be something seriously wrong.

2. At *nightfall*, you might be doing early evening activities, such as eating dinner or doing homework.

3. No, *portions* means "parts," so parts of the bridge would be gone. You need a complete bridge in order to cross safely.

4. You could learn how the person chooses friends and which qualities are most important in a friend because the person's friends would be good examples.

5. No, *historical* means "having to do with history," which is the record of things that have happened in the past, not in the future.

6. You would be unable to solve the problem because *mystified* means "confused or unable to understand."

Reading Warm-up A, p. 88

Sample Answers

1. passed through; The thick trees blocked the sunlight.

2. (marks); He is upset about his *scuffed* sneakers because they were almost new and now they will look worn and dirty.

3. (face); high

4. (shriveled); *Fresh* is an antonym for *wilted*.

5. (The day was fading); Ray needed to move quickly because *sundown* is the time of day when the sun sets, so it would soon be dark and they would need the fire to see and stay warm.

6. (made certain); The pit was lined with large, round stones. . . .

7. (shiny); A *glossy* magazine has thick paper and lots of photographs.

8. to thank nature for a bountiful fall; It might be a Native American tradition or a harvest tradition.

Reading Warm-up B, p. 89

Sample Answers

1. People are born and people die every day; *Nonstop* is a synonym for *continuous*.

2. Beliefs concerning the dead; A tradition at our school is to recognize students for good citizenship, and it is *exhibited* through a monthly award ceremony.

3. (confusion); how workers without modern tools created those enormous stone structures

4. *Historical* experts need a knowledge of history—and often of a specific period of history; (archaeologists)

5. (urgent need); It is *imperative* for a student to do homework and pay attention in class in order to be successful in school.

6. (dark); Early morning, or dawn, is the opposite time of day to *nightfall.*

7. whether a particular custom is "right" or "wrong"; A *judgment* is an opinion because it involves looking at a situation and forming an idea about it.

8. (parts); *Segments* is a synonym for *portions.*

Literary Analysis: Setting, p. 90

Sample Answers

"The Man to Send Rain Clouds"

1. Physical surroundings: dry desert; cottonwood trees; sandy arroyo; high blue mountains covered in snow; highway; mesa; pueblo

2. Time: winter; modern times (pickup truck; highway)

3. Culture: feather; face paint; sprinkling of corn meal; candles; medicine bags; ceremonial dance; holy water; cloistered nuns; priest

4. Overall importance: The blending of two religions in a small desert community is at the heart of the story.

"Old Man of the Temple"

5. Physical surroundings: village of Koopal in South India; late at night; ruined temple; jungle; family with lamps at cottage

6. Time: modern car and driver; night; King Vishnu Varma five centuries ago

7. Culture: hints of reincarnation; belief in spirits; belief that dead souls can transfer into another body; piety of old man who single-handedly built Hindu temple

8. Overall importance: Fantastic elements in the story rely on the cultural setting of Hindu religious beliefs and on the mysterious mood created by the physical setting.

Vocabulary Builder, p. 91

A. Sample Answers

1. His determination to break school rules is so perverse that the principal sent him a letter of warning.

2. He was really disappointed when he discovered that his well-laid plans had gone awry.

3. When we saw how easily they negotiated skiing down the steep slope, we were impressed by their venture.

4. Her winter jacket is so light and flimsy that the bitingly cold wind penetrated it easily.

B. 1. A; 2. C; 3. B; 4. B

Selection Test A, p. 93

Critical Reading

1. ANS: D	DIF: Easy	OBJ: Literary Analysis
2. ANS: C	DIF: Easy	OBJ: Comprehension
3. ANS: A	DIF: Easy	OBJ: Literary Analysis
4. ANS: B	DIF: Easy	OBJ: Comprehension
5. ANS: C	DIF: Easy	OBJ: Interpretation
6. ANS: B	DIF: Easy	OBJ: Interpretation
7. ANS: B	DIF: Easy	OBJ: Literary Analysis
8. ANS: A	DIF: Easy	OBJ: Comprehension
9. ANS: C	DIF: Easy	OBJ: Comprehension
10. ANS: B	DIF: Easy	OBJ: Literary Analysis
11. ANS: D	DIF: Easy	OBJ: Literary Analysis
12. ANS: C	DIF: Easy	OBJ: Interpretation

Vocabulary

| 13. ANS: B | DIF: Easy | OBJ: Vocabulary |
| 14. ANS: D | DIF: Easy | OBJ: Vocabulary |

Essay

15. Students should recognize that the location and cultural background in both stories are key factors. In "The Man to Send Rain Clouds," the story explores conflicts between Pueblo Indian beliefs and Roman Catholic beliefs. In "Old Man of the Temple," the "return" of the long-dead priest is narrated against a background of Hindu beliefs in reincarnation and the transfer of souls from one body to another.

Difficulty: *Easy*
Objective: *Essay*

16. Students should clearly identify two character traits for each main character. In "The Man to Send Rain Clouds," they may mention that Leon is portrayed as patient, polite, and loyal to traditional Pueblo beliefs. In "Old Man of the Temple," the narrator is characterized as patient, resourceful, and compassionate. Look for examples to support each trait students identify.

Difficulty: *Easy*
Objective: *Essay*

8. ANS: C	DIF: Average	OBJ: Comprehension
9. ANS: B	DIF: Challenging	OBJ: Interpretation
10. ANS: A	DIF: Average	OBJ: Literary Analysis
11. ANS: C	DIF: Average	OBJ: Interpretation
12. ANS: B	DIF: Average	OBJ: Interpretation
13. ANS: A	DIF: Average	OBJ: Literary Analysis
14. ANS: B	DIF: Average	OBJ: Literary Analysis

Vocabulary

15. ANS: A	DIF: Average	OBJ: Vocabulary
16. ANS: C	DIF: Average	OBJ: Vocabulary
17. ANS: B	DIF: Challenging	OBJ: Vocabulary

Essay

18. Students should note that the setting in both stories involves a particular culture and belief system. In "The Man to Send Rain Clouds," the cultural setting in New Mexico reveals a conflict between the Pueblo Indians and a Roman Catholic missionary, Father Paul. The setting is linked to the conflict over different rituals for the dead conducted by each group. In "Old Man of the Temple," the narrator's rational expectations are pitted against the fantastical transformation of the driver Doss into an elderly temple priest who should have died at least 500 years ago. In this case, Hindu religious beliefs underlie the story.

Difficulty: *Challenging*
Objective: *Essay*

19. Students should point out that Ken, Leon, and Louise, the leading Native American characters in "The Man to Send Rain Clouds," view death with dignified acceptance. From Leon's thoughts at the end of the story, we can infer that the Pueblos believe that Teofilo will be an active spirit after death and will send the Pueblos rain to ensure the fruitfulness of the land. In "Old Man of the Temple," the old man protests against the finality of death. The narrator's reactions to the old man suggest that he, too, accepts the reality of reincarnation and the passage of souls into other bodies.

Difficulty: *Average*
Objective: *Essay*

Selection Test B, p. 96

Critical Reading

1. ANS: C	DIF: Average	OBJ: Literary Analysis
2. ANS: C	DIF: Average	OBJ: Interpretation
3. ANS: A	DIF: Average	OBJ: Comprehension
4. ANS: A	DIF: Average	OBJ: Literary Analysis
5. ANS: D	DIF: Challenging	OBJ: Interpretation
6. ANS: A	DIF: Average	OBJ: Comprehension
7. ANS: B	DIF: Average	OBJ: Literary Analysis

Writing Workshop—Unit 2, Part 1

Review of a Short Story: Integrating Grammar Skills, p. 100

A. 1. reached; 2. had climbed; 3. will leave

B. Last week, my cousin Lucille and I attended a concert. Lucille had purchased the tickets months before. We walked across the park and hopped on a bus to the concert hall. By the time we arrived, the music had already started. Still, we both enjoyed the concert very much.

Unit 2, Part 1 Answers

Benchmark Test 3, p. 101

MULTIPLE CHOICE

1. ANS: C
2. ANS: D
3. ANS: B
4. ANS: D
5. ANS: D
6. ANS: A
7. ANS: C
8. ANS: B
9. ANS: A
10. ANS: C
11. ANS: C
12. ANS: B
13. ANS: D
14. ANS: B
15. ANS: A
16. ANS: C
17. ANS: A
18. ANS: D
19. ANS: B
20. ANS: D
21. ANS: C
22. ANS: B
23. ANS: D
24. ANS: A
25. ANS: C
26. ANS: D
27. ANS: D
28. ANS: D
29. ANS: C
30. ANS: D
31. ANS: A
32. ANS: B
33. ANS: B

ESSAY

34. Students' fairy tales should demonstrate an understanding of setting and other elements of a short story. It should also demonstrate students' ability to write an alternate ending.

35. Students' outlines should indicate a clear conflict and logical resolution. The outlines should feature two characters who could be further developed in a short story.

36. Students' news stories should be written in the third person, be free of editorializing, and include reports of suggestions for preservation of the chosen species.

Unit 2, Part 2 Answers

Diagnostic Test 4, p. 108

1. ANS: D
2. ANS: D
3. ANS: B
4. ANS: D
5. ANS: A
6. ANS: C
7. ANS: A
8. ANS: D
9. ANS: A
10. ANS: D
11. ANS: C
12. ANS: C
13. ANS: C
14. ANS: A
15. ANS: A

"The Necklace" by Guy de Maupassant

Vocabulary Warm-up Exercises, p. 112

A.
1. outraged
2. distress
3. tormented
4. estimating
5. anguish
6. gracious
7. homemade
8. pitiful

B. Sample Answers

1. *computations*: According to our *computations*, we paid too much.
2. *coworkers*: My *coworkers* and I had a meeting with our boss.
3. *stylish*: Her *stylish* outfit looked as if it came straight out of a magazine.
4. *delicate*: We handled the *delicate* glassware with great care.
5. *money*: We lacked the *money* we needed for the field trip.
6. *worthiest*: This charity has the *worthiest* goals of any group I know.
7. *modest*: Lincoln rose from *modest* beginnings to become president.

Reading Warm-up A, p. 113

Sample Answers

1. I'll likely never afford; A synonym for *gracious* is *elegant*.
2. (pained); She is feeling *anguish* because she wants the earrings so badly it "hurts."
3. that her aunt knitted for her; My mom bakes delicious *homemade* pies.
4. (poor old sweater); My meager allowance is *pitiful*.
5. She feels *tormented* because she thinks her friend is being stingy by not offering to lend her things. Using the word *tormented*, which is really an exaggeration, shows just how strongly Ellie is affected by her friend's reluctance to lend the earrings.
6. (whispered uneasily); I would feel *distress* if my cat became ill.
7. (my hesitant response); I was *outraged* when I was falsely accused of breaking the lawn mower.
8. (number); *Estimating* means "judging the amount of something."

Reading Warm-up B, p. 114

Sample Answers

1. (rings, necklaces); My mother wore her *fashionable* new dress to a party.
2. (jeweler); My *colleagues* are the other students in my class and the other members of my soccer team.
3. a better deal; I was able to get a great price on my new bike by *bargaining* with the storeowner.
4. (a diamond's quality); I do *calculations* when I try to figure out how many weeks I have to work to earn enough money for my prom dress.
5. Although diamonds are very hard, they can be easily damaged by a careless cutter. In that way, they are *fragile*.
6. (most beautiful); The *grandest* thing I have seen lately is my uncle's new car.
7. If you lack *funds*, you can buy a less-expensive alternative such as white topaz. *Money* is a synonym for *funds*.
8. (imitators); They are *humble* because they do not have the same high quality as real diamonds; they are not the real thing.

"The Necklace" by Guy de Maupassant

Literary Analysis: Character and Characterization, p. 115

Sample Answers

1. Madame Loisel is self-centered and materialistic.
2. She treats her husband impatiently and tactlessly; her thoughts revolve only around herself.
3. Monsieur Loisel is patient and tolerant; he places a high value on his wife's happiness.
4. Madame Forestier is snobbish and cold.

5. Madame Loisel is unsure of herself; years of deprivation have eroded her confidence.

Reading: Ask Questions to Analyze Cause and Effect, p. 116

Sample Answers

A. 1. Monsieur Loisel receives an invitation to a reception at the Ministry./ Madame Loisel complains that she has nothing to wear.
2. Monsieur Loisel gives his wife money he had been saving for a gun./ She buys a beautiful dress.
3. She complains that she needs some jewelry./ She borrows a diamond necklace from her friend.
4. She loses her friend's necklace./ The Loisels are forced to borrow a large amount of money in order to replace the necklace.
5. They endure ten years of deprivation to repay the loans./ The hard life ruins Madame Loisel's looks.
6. Madame Loisel sees Madame Forestier and tells her about the lost necklace./ Madame Forestier tells Madame Loisel that the diamonds were fake.

B. Guy de Maupassant suggests that, to a certain extent, Madame Loisel's attitudes are a product of her society. Madame Loisel's rich friend Madame Forestier, for example, is portrayed as superficial. However, Madame Loisel also has her own personal outlook to blame. She is portrayed as self-centered, vain, and materialistic. Her husband, by contrast, is affectionate and satisfied with the couple's lot in life.

Vocabulary Builder, p. 117

Sample Answers

A. 1. A disheveled person would have messy hair and dirty, rumpled clothes.
2. I would feel very sad and regret that I hadn't said or done something.
3. Seeing my little brother play a solo in a piano recital would move strongly. I would feel proud and happy.
4. The most resplendent scene I can think of is the New York City Fourth of July fireworks I watch on TV.

B. 1. The actors' resplendent costumes and masks profoundly impressed us.
2. I felt rueful about my sister's disheveled appearance at the party.

C. 1. C; 2. A; 3. C; 4. B

Enrichment: Defining Values, p. 120

Sample Answers

1. Madame Loisel and Madame Forestier value money, jewels, and high society. Madame Loisel envies Madame Forestier and spends all her time thinking about being wealthy.

2. Monsieur Loisel's husband is satisfied with his simple life. He loves his wife and goes out of his way to try to make her happy.

3. Yes. Madame Loisel's experience might teach her to be more appreciative of her old life. Also, she might realize that wealth and high society are not so important after all.

Selection Test A, p. 121

Critical Reading

1. ANS: B	DIF: Easy	OBJ: Comprehension
2. ANS: B	DIF: Easy	OBJ: Reading
3. ANS: D	DIF: Easy	OBJ: Literary Analysis
4. ANS: D	DIF: Easy	OBJ: Literary Analysis
5. ANS: A	DIF: Easy	OBJ: Literary Analysis
6. ANS: D	DIF: Easy	OBJ: Interpretation
7. ANS: D	DIF: Easy	OBJ: Comprehension
8. ANS: D	DIF: Easy	OBJ: Reading
9. ANS: B	DIF: Easy	OBJ: Comprehension
10. ANS: B	DIF: Easy	OBJ: Interpretation
11. ANS: A	DIF: Easy	OBJ: Interpretation
12. ANS: C	DIF: Easy	OBJ: Interpretation

Vocabulary and Grammar

13. ANS: C	DIF: Easy	OBJ: Vocabulary
14. ANS: C	DIF: Easy	OBJ: Vocabulary
15. ANS: D	DIF: Easy	OBJ: Grammar

Essay

16. Students' essays should address how the necklace represents the materialistic mindset of Madame Loisel. Ironically, she must give up her materialistic goals in order to replace the lost necklace. The necklace has a great impact on her life in many ways: for example, the hard work she is forced to undertake, the couple's move to an attic apartment, and the extra jobs Monsieur Loisel takes on in order to repay the huge debt. Students should identify the story's theme as an ironic commentary on people's mistaken priorities.

Difficulty: *Easy*

Objective: *Essay*

17. Students should note that Madame Loisel treats her husband with resentment and hostility. She would rather have married a man of wealth and social status. Her treatment of him shows that she values money and position more than love. It also shows her to be self-centered. Her husband, on the other hand, repeatedly makes sacrifices to try to please her. He obviously places her feelings above his own, and he seems satisfied with their humble existence.

Difficulty: *Easy*

Objective: *Essay*

Selection Test B, p. 124

Critical Reading

1. ANS: B	DIF: Average	OBJ: Reading
2. ANS: D	DIF: Average	OBJ: Literary Analysis
3. ANS: B	DIF: Average	OBJ: Literary Analysis
4. ANS: D	DIF: Challenging	OBJ: Literary Analysis
5. ANS: A	DIF: Average	OBJ: Literary Analysis
6. ANS: C	DIF: Challenging	OBJ: Interpretation
7. ANS: A	DIF: Challenging	OBJ: Reading
8. ANS: D	DIF: Average	OBJ: Comprehension
9. ANS: D	DIF: Average	OBJ: Reading
10. ANS: B	DIF: Challenging	OBJ: Interpretation
11. ANS: C	DIF: Challenging	OBJ: Interpretation
12. ANS: B	DIF: Average	OBJ: Interpretation
13. ANS: B	DIF: Average	OBJ: Comprehension
14. ANS: A	DIF: Average	OBJ: Interpretation

Vocabulary and Grammar

15. ANS: C	DIF: Average	OBJ: Vocabulary
16. ANS: A	DIF: Challenging	OBJ: Vocabulary
17. ANS: B	DIF: Average	OBJ: Vocabulary
18. ANS: D	DIF: Average	OBJ: Grammar
19. ANS: C	DIF: Average	OBJ: Grammar
20. ANS: A	DIF: Average	OBJ: Grammar

Essay

21. Students' essays should explain that Madame Loisel is characterized as vain and materialistic. Dissatisfied with her circumstances, she wishes for a sparkling, wealthy life of pleasure and luxury. However, her desperate pursuit of this lifestyle leads her to a life of regret, poverty, and hard work. In the same way, the necklace Madame Loisel borrows appears to be expensive and desirable, but it is in fact false and not worth the suffering it causes the Loisels. The necklace also symbolizes the shallowness of a society that places such importance on the appearance of wealth. The necklace thus relates to the story's theme, which concerns the foolishness and danger of attaching too much importance to wealth.

Difficulty: *Average*

Objective: *Essay*

22. Students should note that Madame Loisel treats her husband with resentment and hostility; she would rather have married a man of wealth and social status. Her treatment of him shows that she values money and position more than love; it also shows her to be self-centered. Her husband, on the other hand, repeatedly makes sacrifices to try to please her. He obviously places

her feelings above his own, and he seems satisfied with their humble existence.

Difficulty: *Average*
Objective: *Essay*

"Rules of the Game" by Amy Tan

Vocabulary Warm-up Exercises, p. 128

A.
1. essential
2. triumphant
3. trophy
4. chess
5. deliberately
6. concealed
7. relented
8. proclaimed

B. Sample Answers
1. My mother would have *encased* her wedding china because it was fragile and she would want it to be protected.
2. A breakfast *menu* might feature pancakes, eggs, waffles, and juice.
3. If my view were *obscured*, I would stop and pull over because I would not be able to see where I was going.
4. If I liked the sharp aroma, I might get hungry. Otherwise, I might find the *pungent* smell unpleasant.
5. A *protective* mother would guard her children from harm. She would keep them warm and safe.
6. They might call the local police or a town official to handle a *regional* problem.
7. A *specialized* library might have a collection of books or recordings related to a particular topic. For example, it might specialize in photography books or jazz recordings.
8. You probably should *reveal* your true feelings because otherwise the person you are seeking advice from will not know how you really feel about the matter.

Reading Warm-up A, p. 129

Sample Answers
1. (game); I enjoy checkers and backgammon.
2. (the best players), (highly honored); *Proclaimed* means "officially announced."
3. tell their secrets; They may have *relented* because of having been pressured by the other masters.
4. the growing popularity of the game; The books were *essential* because chess could not become popular unless people knew how to play it.
5. (Paul Morphy); I would like to be *triumphant* in the National Spelling Bee.
6. (dominate world chess); I *deliberately* put the cough medicine on a high shelf so my baby sister could not reach it.

7. (world championship); The Russian players probably felt disgraced for having lost the championship and the *trophy*.
8. (hide); Kasparov probably *concealed* his disappointment by smiling a lot and pretending that he was not upset over his loss.

Reading Warm-up B, p. 130

Sample Answers
1. (unusual objects of every description); The museum *encased* all the pieces of pottery that were a hundred years old.
2. Others concentrate on one specific kind of item; I like the store at the mall that has *specialized* in fruit juice shakes.
3. different areas of China; The grapes that grow in the local vineyard are one example of a *regional* product.
4. the kinds of things being offered for sale; *Reveal* means "make known or display."
5. If you do not look at the *menu*, you might find out that the restaurant does not serve anything you are interested in eating.
6. (smell of incense); Other *pungent* things are the smell of curried food and the taste of garlic.
7. The bridge might be *obscured* because thick fog might make it hard to see. *Obscured* means "prevented from being seen or heard."
8. the parents and grandparents of Chinatown; I am *protective* of my younger brother.

"Rules of the Game" by Amy Tan

Literary Analysis: Character and Characterization, p. 131

Sample Answers
1. Mrs. Jong wants her children to lead a better life than she and her husband do.
2. Mrs. Jong is proud and unwilling to accept a secondhand gift.
3. Mrs. Jong takes vicarious pleasure in Meimei's success. At the same time, Meimei is embarrassed and annoyed by her mother's overprotective attitude.
4. Mrs. Jong's pride finds an outlet through her daughter.

Reading: Ask Questions to Analyze Cause and Effect, p. 132

Sample Answers
2. Vincent and Winston play chess a lot./ Meimei becomes fascinated by the game.
3. Meimei plays chess with Lau Po./ Her game steadily improves.
4. She enters local chess tournaments./ She wins many trophies.

5. She enters larger tournaments./ She becomes a national chess champion.

6. Mrs. Jong smothers Meimei with attention and extra privileges./ Meimei becomes increasingly annoyed with her mother.

7. Meimei accuses her mother of showing off./ Mrs. Jong and Meimei quarrel.

Vocabulary Builder, p. 133

Sample Answers

A. 1. The dish tastes spicy.

2. I am speaking sharply.

3. I would not choose to eat there because the bad smell would make me nauseous and spoil my meal.

4. I would feel happy if a classmate looked at me benevolently.

B. 1. Their pungent criticism tempted us to retort, but we held our tongue.

2. When we entered, the restaurant owner smiled benevolently, but the malodorous atmosphere caused us to leave promptly.

C. 1. C; 2. A; 3. B; 4. D

Enrichment: Performing Arts, p. 136

Sample Answers

1. To acquire skill in a performing art such as instrumental music, students may list the need to practice and to take lessons from an experienced instrumentalist. Steps for improving skill might include choosing an even more experienced teacher, more practice (both alone and in a group), listening to experienced instrumentalists, playing increasingly challenging pieces, and so on.

2. Students' steps for acquiring skill may not include reading about a performing art, because reading about playing a trumpet, for example, is far less helpful than reading about chess. Students should note a similar progression, though, in terms of acquiring skill and beginning to apply skill.

3. Whereas Waverly was able to improve her skills by playing increasingly challenging opponents, students may improve a performing arts skill by challenging themselves to be better actors, musicians, etc., and to take on more difficult roles or musical selections. Visualization and imagination may play a part in a performer's training—a dancer visualizes a perfect leap or a flutist imagines exactly how a passage should sound.

4. Students should conclude that commitment and self-discipline play a large role in any such pursuit, both in terms of the actual time spent practicing and in the physical and mental resources devoted to the project. Students may point out that if one is truly talented at or passionate about something, whether it be playing chess or playing the piano, the commitment and self-discipline would come relatively easily.

"Rules of the Game" by Amy Tan
"The Necklace" by Guy de Maupassant

Build Language Skills: Vocabulary, p. 137

Word Roots
Sample Answers

A. 1. *-ver-*

You can verify those statistics by consulting an almanac.

2. *-ver-*

The author's use of dialect gives the story verisimilitude.

3. *-vert-*

The rebels' goal is the subversion of the elected government.

4. *-verd-*

She likes to walk through the verdant public gardens.

5. *-vert-*

The painting is all red except for one black vertical line.

B. 1. A flashback interrupts the sequence of events to narrate an earlier event.

2. An essay's title often announces or hints at the writer's topic.

3. *Enthusiastic, humorous, ironic,* and *critical* might describe an author's attitude.

4. You can verify cause-and-effect relationships by reviewing plot details.

5. Quotation marks imply that the sentence represents the exact words of a speaker.

Build Language Skills: Grammar, p. 138

Action and Linking Verbs, Transitive and Intransitive Verbs
Sample Answers

A. 1. An action verb expresses physical or mental actions.

2. Wayne swam easily from one end of the pool to the other.

3. A linking verb connects the subject to a word that renames or describes the subject.

4. Despite the turbulence, we remained calm.

5. A transitive verb is an action verb that directs action toward someone or something named in the same sentence: Ross scored his first soccer goal.

An intransitive verb is an action verb that does not direct action toward something or someone named in the same sentence: Ross plays for the Planco Veterinary Care team.

B. 1. B; 2. A; 3. A; 4. B

"Rules of the Game" by Amy Tan

Selection Test A, p. 139

Critical Reading

1. ANS: D	DIF: Easy	OBJ: Comprehension
2. ANS: B	DIF: Easy	OBJ: Reading
3. ANS: C	DIF: Easy	OBJ: Literary Analysis
4. ANS: C	DIF: Easy	OBJ: Interpretation
5. ANS: C	DIF: Easy	OBJ: Reading
6. ANS: C	DIF: Easy	OBJ: Interpretation
7. ANS: D	DIF: Easy	OBJ: Interpretation
8. ANS: D	DIF: Easy	OBJ: Literary Analysis
9. ANS: C	DIF: Easy	OBJ: Comprehension
10. ANS: C	DIF: Easy	OBJ: Comprehension
11. ANS: B	DIF: Easy	OBJ: Interpretation

Vocabulary and Grammar

12. ANS: A	DIF: Easy	OBJ: Vocabulary
13. ANS: A	DIF: Easy	OBJ: Vocabulary
14. ANS: A	DIF: Easy	OBJ: Grammar
15. ANS: D	DIF: Easy	OBJ: Grammar

Essay

16. Students should point out that Mrs. Jong emphasizes that immigrants must know the laws of their new country. Meimei cannot rely on the government or on powerful people to help her achieve her goals. She must learn the "rules of the game" on her own and practice them accordingly.
Difficulty: *Easy*
Objective: *Essay*

17. Students should point out that both Meimei and Mrs. Jong are highly competitive. Both are strong, smart, proud, and ambitious. Mrs. Jong is more Chinese than Chinese American, however, and is devoted to the "old ways." Given their similarities and important differences, students may predict that their conflict will be ongoing. Besides their generational conflict, they are likely to be in conflict about how Americanized Meimei will become.
Difficulty: *Easy*
Objective: *Essay*

Selection Test B, p. 142

Critical Reading

1. ANS: B	DIF: Average	OBJ: Reading
2. ANS: D	DIF: Average	OBJ: Comprehension
3. ANS: C	DIF: Challenging	OBJ: Literary Analysis
4. ANS: C	DIF: Average	OBJ: Interpretation
5. ANS: A	DIF: Challenging	OBJ: Literary Analysis
6. ANS: C	DIF: Average	OBJ: Interpretation
7. ANS: C	DIF: Average	OBJ: Interpretation
8. ANS: B	DIF: Challenging	OBJ: Literary Analysis
9. ANS: D	DIF: Challenging	OBJ: Interpretation
10. ANS: D	DIF: Challenging	OBJ: Reading
11. ANS: B	DIF: Challenging	OBJ: Interpretation
12. ANS: C	DIF: Average	OBJ: Comprehension
13. ANS: C	DIF: Average	OBJ: Comprehension
14. ANS: B	DIF: Average	OBJ: Interpretation

Vocabulary and Grammar

15. ANS: C	DIF: Challenging	OBJ: Vocabulary
16. ANS: B	DIF: Challenging	OBJ: Vocabulary
17. ANS: C	DIF: Average	OBJ: Vocabulary
18. ANS: A	DIF: Average	OBJ: Grammar
19. ANS: C	DIF: Average	OBJ: Grammar
20. ANS: A	DIF: Challenging	OBJ: Grammar

Essay

21. Students should begin with a description of the setting: Chinatown in San Francisco. They should cite details from the author's account of the alley, with its marvels and mysteries; the smells; the playground; the shops. The setting is, in effect, an entire world. It gives readers a sense of the culture of the characters which, in turn, helps readers understand why the characters think and behave as they do.
Difficulty: *Average*
Objective: *Essay*

22. Students should point out that, while the story is dominated by a serious and stressful conflict between generations, Tan uses numerous light touches to moderate the tone. Among these devices are Mrs. Jong's "fractured English," the descriptions of the children's games and pranks, the fanciful names for chess moves, and Mrs. Jong's pseudo-humility at the tournaments ("Is luck"). Overall, students may conclude that the story includes considerable humor.
Difficulty: *Challenging*
Objective: *Essay*

"Blues Ain't No Mockin Bird"
by Toni Cade Bambara

Vocabulary Warm-up Exercises, p. 146

A. 1. spooky
   2. mortal
   3. ladle
   4. original
   5. mental

6. grumpy
7. grove
8. breeding

B. Sample Answers

1. F; If you *consider* ordering a pizza, it means that you are thinking about it.

2. F; *Amongst* means you are with your friends, and since they are your friends, you probably feel comfortable with them.

3. T; Holding rallies for sports teams might be part of a series of activities with the goal of improving school spirit.

4. T; If leaves are crunching *underfoot*, you are stepping on them and must be walking. Also, it is usually in the fall when leaves are dry enough to make a crunching sound.

5. F; *Speckled* means "covered in small specks or marks," and if you fell and rolled in the mud, you would have more than specks on you.

6. F; *Misery* is a state of extreme unhappiness or suffering, and it is not something that could be easily changed.

7. F; *Reckless* is the opposite of being responsible because you are not being careful about the consequences of your decisions or behavior.

8. T; Both are needed for these items to work. A traditional camera does not take photos without *film*, and a traditional car does not run without gasoline.

Reading Warm-up A, p. 147

Sample Answers

1. told her to hurry; (he was tired from packing)

2. (mind; thoughts); A *mental* image is a picture you form in your mind.

3. (manners); Ned pressed his face onto the window with his nose pushed up

4. (extreme); Being in *mortal* fear would be feeling so afraid that you might think you are going to die.

5. (odd); I think it is *spooky* when I am thinking of a friend and that person suddenly calls me—it is as though we can communicate through our thoughts.

6. (trees); A *grove* would have many trees, probably of the same type, growing together.

7. (new); If I have an *original* idea, it means the idea is not copied from someone else and is probably creative and different.

8. (spooned out); Any kind of food that contains a lot of liquid, such as soup, stew, or gravy, would be served with a *ladle*.

Reading Warm-up B, p. 148

Sample Answers

1. millions who lost their jobs and often their homes; *Happiness* is an antonym for *misery*.

2. (camera); images were captured

3. document the living conditions of migrant laborers; (series of efforts)

4. (irresponsibly); If a friend was being *reckless*, I would talk to him or her and point out the behavior that could lead to problems for him or her.

5. Many failed to *consider* that the soil might get worn out. The "dust bowl" was the result.

6. Lange was with the people, where they lived and worked, to photograph *amongst* them.

7. (children); In this sentence, *underfoot* might mean that they were huddled around her feet on the ground, not that she was stepping on them.

8. The children who were *speckled* with dirt would not be completely dirty but would have specks or marks of dirt on their faces, arms, hands, and clothing.

"Blues Ain't No Mockin Bird"
by Toni Cade Bambara

Literary Analysis: Dialogue and Dialect, p. 149

Sample Answers

A.
1. Camera's use of "aunty" reveals that he is patronizing Granny—feeling superior to her. Granny's sharp reply indicates that she is capable of standing up for herself.

2. Granny's story shows that she has a gift for teaching by examples. It also reveals that she is compassionate and sympathetic with other people's hardships.

3. Granddaddy is blunt, direct, and dignified. He is proud of owning property.

B.
1. Granny wasn't saying anything.

2. Cathy and I were waiting, too, because Granny always had something to say.

3. Granny just stared at the twins until their faces showed no more eagerness and they didn't even care any more about the man jumping.

Reading: Visualize the Action to Analyze Cause and Effect, p. 150

Sample Answers

1. A. She tells the story to point out the similar rudeness and lack of respect shown by Camera and Smilin.
   B. One effect of the story is to shock the twins into silence. Granny's story also motivates Cathy to tell the story of Goldilocks.

2. A. The hawk wants to claim its dying mate, who has been wounded and captured by Granddaddy Cain.
   B. The hawk terrifies them and throws them into confusion.
   C. He calmly throws a hammer at the hawk and kills it.

3. A. They are standing in Granny's flower bed. Furthermore, they have taken pictures of the house and the family without permission.
   B. They are confused and frightened, and they back away.

Vocabulary Builder, p. 151

Sample Answers

A. 1. Yes. I would be worried that he would cause an accident and injure someone as well as damage the car.

2. Politeness. Someone who treats me with formality would be courteous and follow the rules of polite behavior.

B. 1. When he reached the corner, Carlos grew reckless and crossed the street against the light.

2. In Europe and Japan, children are taught to treat their elders with formality.

C. 1. C; 2. B

Enrichment: Journalism, p. 154

A. Students' questions should focus on journalists' use of a code of ethics. Questions should be direct without being invasive. (An example of an invasive question is, "Have you ever acted unethically?") You might model the following question to demonstrate the kind of ethical decisions a responsible journalist makes: "Have you ever lost a story because you couldn't pursue it in an ethical manner?"

B. Limiting students' presentations to several minutes will force them to summarize rather than to relate whole interviews. For students who obtained permission to tape interviews, suggest that they take notes to help them sift information and organize their summaries. Have students work with peer reviewers to make sure that the facts, details, and anecdotes in their summaries all support the main idea—their code of ethics.

Selection Test A, p. 155

Critical Reading

1. ANS: A	DIF: Easy	OBJ: Comprehension
2. ANS: C	DIF: Easy	OBJ: Literary Analysis
3. ANS: B	DIF: Easy	OBJ: Reading
4. ANS: D	DIF: Easy	OBJ: Interpretation
5. ANS: B	DIF: Easy	OBJ: Interpretation
6. ANS: B	DIF: Easy	OBJ: Reading
7. ANS: C	DIF: Easy	OBJ: Comprehension
8. ANS: B	DIF: Easy	OBJ: Comprehension
9. ANS: B	DIF: Easy	OBJ: Reading
10. ANS: B	DIF: Easy	OBJ: Literary Analysis
11. ANS: C	DIF: Easy	OBJ: Interpretation

Vocabulary and Grammar

12. ANS: A	DIF: Easy	OBJ: Vocabulary
13. ANS: B	DIF: Easy	OBJ: Vocabulary
14. ANS: C	DIF: Easy	OBJ: Grammar
15. ANS: B	DIF: Easy	OBJ: Grammar

Essay

16. Students should note that Granny is a strong woman who is not afraid to express her opinions and defend her own rights, as, for example, when she tells the cameramen to shut off their camera. Often Granny's silences speak louder than words: she stares at the cameramen and gets them to leave. Students may note that Granny's low and grumpy mumbling indicates her intense upset.

Difficulty: *Easy*

Objective: *Essay*

17. Students should note that the dialogue establishes the conflict and reveals the character of Granny and her husband. Most students will say that they enjoyed the dialogue and dialect. Both help to bring the characters to life and make them more believable.

Difficulty: *Easy*

Objective: *Essay*

Selection Test B, p. 158

Critical Reading

1. ANS: A	DIF: Average	OBJ: Comprehension
2. ANS: B	DIF: Average	OBJ: Reading
3. ANS: B	DIF: Average	OBJ: Literary Analysis
4. ANS: C	DIF: Average	OBJ: Literary Analysis
5. ANS: D	DIF: Challenging	OBJ: Interpretation
6. ANS: D	DIF: Average	OBJ: Interpretation
7. ANS: B	DIF: Challenging	OBJ: Reading
8. ANS: C	DIF: Average	OBJ: Comprehension
9. ANS: B	DIF: Average	OBJ: Interpretation
10. ANS: A	DIF: Average	OBJ: Comprehension
11. ANS: B	DIF: Average	OBJ: Reading
12. ANS: D	DIF: Challenging	OBJ: Interpretation
13. ANS: C	DIF: Average	OBJ: Comprehension

Vocabulary and Grammar

14. ANS: A	DIF: Average	OBJ: Vocabulary
15. ANS: B	DIF: Average	OBJ: Vocabulary
16. ANS: D	DIF: Average	OBJ: Literary Analysis
17. ANS: A	DIF: Average	OBJ: Grammar
18. ANS: B	DIF: Average	OBJ: Grammar
19. ANS: D	DIF: Average	OBJ: Grammar

Essay

20. Student essays should point out that dialogue helps to characterize Granny, Granddaddy, the children, and the two reporters. Dialogue also helps to move the plot forward, as when Granny asks Granddaddy Cain to get the

reporters out of her flower bed. Finally, the use of dialect in the story gives the narrative a vivid, local flavor.

Difficulty: *Average*

Objective: *Essay*

21. Students' essays should note that the packing incident reveals Granddaddy Cain as loyal to his wife and angered by other people's treatment. The hawk incident reveals that he is calm, cool, and skillful as he brings down the hawk. That prepares the reader for his interaction with the reporters: he is commanding, "tall and silent and like a king," as he demands the camera, ruins the film, and gets them to leave.

Difficulty: *Challenging*

Objective: *Essay*

"The Invalid's Story" by Mark Twain

Vocabulary Warm-up Exercises, p. 162

A. 1. railway
2. ambition
3. considerable
4. impressed
5. distressed
6. drenched
7. stifling
8. cheerless

B. Sample Answers
1. F; *Placidly* means "calmly," so you would more likely not be in a hurry.
2. T; A friend who is *overdue* is later than expected, and that might indicate a problem and be cause for worry.
3. F; *Pathetic* means "causing pity or sorrow," and a good player would be the opposite of that.
4. F; Groups that were working together would need to hold at least one *consultation* to share ideas and make a plan.
5. T; War and poverty both cause a great deal of pain, distress, and other *sufferings*.
6. F; An animal with good hearing would be able to *detect*, or notice, a low sound.
7. F; *Unendurable* means "not able to be endured or tolerated," and problems that big are not easy to solve.
8. F; A *remembrance* helps us remember a relative who has died; it is usually a solemn occasion, not a time for celebrating.

Reading Warm-up A, p. 163

Sample Answers
1. (train); I have never ridden in a *railway* car, but I have seen many as trains passed by.
2. great deal; *Substantial* is a synonym for *considerable*.
3. desire; My *ambition* is to be a successful professional.

4. (very upset); *Delighted* is an antonym for *distressed*.
5. Who would not admire a railroad car with leather seats, lamps with silk shades, and chandeliers? Who would not enjoy a delicious meal expertly served in an elegant setting? Most people would be *impressed* by my willingness to pitch in and help others, such as by donating time to good causes.
6. Hard seats, poor food, and bad smells awaited those without the money for better. *Miserable* is a synonym for *cheerless*.
7. (hot), (summer); Summer in the city is *stifling*, so my family heads for the beach and its cool ocean waters.
8. (soaked); You would notice a very strong smell because it would mean the person was wearing a lot of cologne.

Reading Warm-up B, p. 164

Sample Answers
1. Twain honored Grant's life by making it possible for Grant to present his autobiography and for others to read it after Grant's death; Memorial Day is a holiday of *remembrance* because U.S. soldiers who have died in all wars are honored on that day.
2. his judgment was very poor in business matters; *Admirable* is an antonym for *pathetic*.
3. Many readers had long expected a book by Grant; If he was writing the book and it was *overdue*, it would mean he was late in finishing it.
4. the two men discussed and agreed on a deal; A *consultation* is a discussion between people who share an interest in something and want to reach agreement on it.
5. (noticed); You may use all of your senses to *detect* because you can notice something you see, smell, hear, taste, or feel.
6. (quietly), (peaceful); Someone living *placidly* in the mountains might spend a lot of time outdoors peacefully enjoying nature.
7. (pain and distress); Grant's *sufferings* would be similar because he was in pain and may have felt fear, like people in war often do.
8. nothing could soothe her misery and help her tolerate that loss; The death of a close friend or family member is *unendurable* for most people.

"The Invalid's Story" by Mark Twain

Literary Analysis: Dialogue and Dialect, p. 165

Sample Answers
A. 1. In this bit of dialogue, Thompson sounds triumphant and determined. The dialogue shows his perseverance.
2. Thompson's words reveal the enjoyment he takes in trying to solve the problem. Students might also say that he is a sports fan and knowledgeable about boxing.

B. 1. "Human beings have short lives, as Scripture says."

2. "Yes, it's very serious and mysterious, but we all have to die one time or another; there's no avoiding it."

Reading: Visualize the Action to Analyze Cause and Effect, p. 166

Sample Answers

A. 1. The narrator feels shocked and sad. He feels he must carry out his friend's last request, which is that he escort the body to Wisconsin.

2. A. He thinks there has been some confusion about the coffin-box, which is mysteriously back on the platform.
   B. The narrator ended up escorting a long white-pine box full of guns.

3. The effects are hilarious: the narrator and the expressman confuse the ripe smell of the cheese with the horrible odor from a decomposing corpse.

4. A. The Limburger cheese causes the odor.
   B. The narrator and the expressman, who think that the odor comes from the corpse, become progressively more disgusted and sickened. They try all sorts of things to lessen the bad smell.

B. Answers will vary. Examine students' responses for examples, reasons, and specific details from the story.

Vocabulary Builder, p. 167

Sample Answers

A. 1. The person would be acting calmly—maybe sitting and reading a book.

2. Weather with deleterious effects, such as a hurricane, would damage a building.

3. Yes. I'd feel confident the person would give me wise advice.

4. If I were climbing an enormous mountain, I'd feel tired and scared.

B. 1. The prodigious torrents of rain that fell last summer had a deleterious effect on our old tool shed.

2. Her manner was extremely judicious as she placidly answered every question in great detail.

C. 1. C; 2. D; 3. C; 4. B

Enrichment: History of American Railroads, p. 170

Sample Answers

1. Students may mention the desire of merchants and factory owners to ship goods to more and larger markets and the desire of farmers and ranchers to ship their goods to large population centers.

2. Landowners often used very aggressive (and sometimes illegal) tactics to buy up land near the new railroad lines. Towns (and merchants) could flourish or wither away depending on their nearness to the railroad lines.

3. The line was completed in May 10, 1869, at Promontory Point, Utah.

4. Pullman invented the sleeping car for passengers, and Westinghouse invented the air brake for railroad cars. Both inventions improved comfort and safety.

5. Students may mention the expanding trucking industry and the expansion of air freight. Passengers preferred airplanes rather than trains in order to cover long distances in a shorter time.

"Blues Ain't No Mockin Bird" by Toni Cade Bambara
"The Invalid's Story" by Mark Twain

Build Language Skills: Vocabulary, p. 171

Word Roots
Sample Answers

A. 1. arranged in a regular order

   The novelist invites his readers to change the sequential order of chapters.

2. following in order

   That textbook follows a consecutive, chronological approach to history.

3. punish; pursue vindictively

   During the third century A.D., the Romans vigorously persecuted Christians.

4. important; significant

   In a consequential decision, the Supreme Court moved to protect the rights of criminal defendants.

5. remark that has nothing to do with what has just been said (literally, "it does not follow")

   When the speaker was asked a question, he replied with a non sequitur and turned away.

B. 1. The *topic* of that magazine article is the urgency of energy conservation.

2. The narrator's *attitude* in that short story is dryly ironic.

3. Lines 1–3 *imply* that the speaker in the poem is on a journey far from home.

4. To *verify* the results, she repeated the experiment several times.

5. To break a code, you must decipher letters or numbers in the proper *sequence*.

Build Language Skills: Grammar, p. 172

Subject and Predicate
Sample Answers

A. 1. The subject of a sentence is the word or group of words telling whom or what the sentence is about.

2. The birds in the golden cage sang delightful melodies.

3. The predicate of a sentence is the word or group of words that expresses an action, a condition, or a state of being.

4. Everyone in our class <u>enjoyed the performance of the play</u>.

5. Subjects and verbs must agree in number. A singular subject takes a singular verb; a plural subject takes a plural verb.

B. Vertical lines should be drawn after the following words:

1. camera; 2. Cathy; 3. Cain; 4. You; 5. I;

6. Thompson; 7. friend; 8. health

"The Invalid's Story" by Mark Twain

Selection Test A, p. 173

Critical Reading

1. ANS: C	DIF: Easy	OBJ: Comprehension
2. ANS: A	DIF: Easy	OBJ: Comprehension
3. ANS: B	DIF: Easy	OBJ: Comprehension
4. ANS: D	DIF: Easy	OBJ: Literary Analysis
5. ANS: D	DIF: Easy	OBJ: Literary Analysis
6. ANS: B	DIF: Easy	OBJ: Interpretation
7. ANS: B	DIF: Easy	OBJ: Interpretation
8. ANS: C	DIF: Easy	OBJ: Literary Analysis
9. ANS: D	DIF: Easy	OBJ: Reading
10. ANS: B	DIF: Easy	OBJ: Comprehension
11. ANS: C	DIF: Easy	OBJ: Reading
12. ANS: A	DIF: Easy	OBJ: Comprehension

Vocabulary and Grammar

13. ANS: C	DIF: Easy	OBJ: Vocabulary
14. ANS: B	DIF: Easy	OBJ: Vocabulary
15. ANS: C	DIF: Easy	OBJ: Grammar

Essay

16. Students' essays should note that as the story progresses, the smell becomes increasingly unbearable and exaggerated. It is the two men's unsuccessful attempts to deal with the problem that create much of the story's humor. Students may mention any of the men's attempted "solutions"—for example, that they smoke cigars or that they stand outside on the platform till they are almost frozen.

Difficulty: *Easy*

Objective: *Literary Analysis*

17. Students should point out that Twain uses dialect in the speeches of Thompson, the expressman. The dialect contributes to humor because its folksy, offhand quality contrasts amusingly with the dreadful situation in which the men find themselves. The use of dialect helps us to hear Thompson's voice quite clearly. It helps to create local color and a sense of realism in the story.

Difficulty: *Easy*

Objective: *Literary Analysis*

Selection Test B, p. 176

Critical Reading

1. ANS: B	DIF: Average	OBJ: Comprehension
2. ANS: C	DIF: Average	OBJ: Comprehension
3. ANS: C	DIF: Average	OBJ: Comprehension
4. ANS: D	DIF: Average	OBJ: Literary Analysis
5. ANS: C	DIF: Challenging	OBJ: Interpretation
6. ANS: D	DIF: Average	OBJ: Literary Analysis
7. ANS: B	DIF: Average	OBJ: Interpretation
8. ANS: C	DIF: Average	OBJ: Literary Analysis
9. ANS: B	DIF: Average	OBJ: Interpretation
10. ANS: A	DIF: Average	OBJ: Literary Analysis
11. ANS: D	DIF: Average	OBJ: Reading
12. ANS: B	DIF: Average	OBJ: Interpretation
13. ANS: A	DIF: Average	OBJ: Comprehension
14. ANS: B	DIF: Average	OBJ: Reading

Vocabulary and Grammar

15. ANS: C	DIF: Average	OBJ: Vocabulary
16. ANS: C	DIF: Average	OBJ: Vocabulary
17. ANS: A	DIF: Challenging	OBJ: Vocabulary
18. ANS: C	DIF: Average	OBJ: Grammar
19. ANS: A	DIF: Average	OBJ: Grammar
20. ANS: D	DIF: Average	OBJ: Grammar

Essay

21. Students' essays should note that when the narrator notices the smell of the corpse, his first reaction is sadness that the smell will be his final concrete memory of his friend. When the train becomes warm and stifling, the smell becomes more unbearable. The descriptions are humorous because they become more and more exaggerated. Thompson's attempts to deal with the problem and his belief that the narrator's friend is purposely creating the smell also add humor to the story.

Difficulty: *Average*

Objective: *Literary Analysis*

22. Students should point out that Twain has the narrator reveal the shift of the gun box for the coffin and the presence of the Limburger cheese at the outset of the story. Thus, the progressively more and more serious discomfort of the narrator and Thompson are set within a context of dramatic irony; the reader knows the truth but the characters do not. The characters' disgust and desperation steadily mount, until they are portrayed in a ludicrous "waltz" in and out of the express car in order to escape the foul smell. The pacing enhances the tension right up to the final paragraph, when the train arrives at its destination.

Difficulty: *Average*

Objective: *Essay*

"The Scarlet Ibis" by James Hurst

"The Golden Kite, the Silver Wind"
by Ray Bradbury

Vocabulary Warm-up Exercises, p. 180

A. 1. hazy
2. exotic
3. discouraged
4. spectacular
5. accidentally
6. awkwardness
7. unbearable
8. monotony

B. Sample Answers

1. No, a *bustling* community is very active and noisy.

2. *Cooperation* means that people are working well together, so, if people were cooperating, a project would probably get done more quickly.

3. The train would probably arrive earlier because it *departed,* or left, the station earlier.

4. People who brag about their *modesty* are not behaving very modestly.

5. No, *omens* of disaster are signs that something bad is going to happen.

6. I would pour water on a bonfire to *quench* it, or put it out.

7. To *sustain* a good reputation, you should maintain it by continuing to behave properly.

8. No, a *paralyzed* person is not able to move.

Reading Warm-up A, p. 181

Sample Answers

1. must have fallen off that bike a hundred times; *Awkwardness* might cause someone to trip or bump into something.

2. (would have wanted to quit); A person might feel *discouraged* if he or she kept getting bad grades.

3. (alien); He is like an *exotic* creature because he is different from everyone else.

4. going to class every day and doing homework every night; *Monotony* means "sameness."

5. with a careless word or deed; A person might *accidentally* break a glass.

6. you just wanted to take the little guy in your arms and give him a great big hug; I think the Christmas tree in Rockefeller Center is *spectacular.*

7. Jason could be so lovable sometimes; *Unbearable* means "too uncomfortable to deal with."

8. (I think); I have a *hazy* memory of the day my younger sister was born.

Reading Warm-up B, p. 182

Sample Answers

1. fear of being overrun by the northern barbarians; *Paralyzed* means "made unable to move."

2. (boastful); Someone who shows great *modesty* about his or her accomplishments does not brag but keeps the sense of achievement to himself or herself.

3. (their own power); *Sustain* means "keep up or maintain."

4. The invasions were seen as *omens* that more invasions were to come, resulting in the eventual conquest of China. *Omens* are warning signs.

5. (work sites); The train station in my community is always *bustling,* or full of noise and activity.

6. Water thrown on a fire would *quench* it, or put it out, because its oxygen supply would be cut off. We had to *quench* our campfire before leaving the campsite.

7. to complete the vast building project; *Cooperation* is needed to produce a school play.

8. (China); We *arrived* early for the performance.

Literary Analysis: Symbol and Allegory, p. 183

Sample Answers

1. The weather symbolically suggests decay, destruction, and death. Even the sun is "thirsty" in this period of unnatural drought.

2. The symbolism emphasizes that the narrator has learned too late about the uniqueness and loving nature of his younger brother, who resembled the ibis in his vulnerability.

3. The passage underscores the spirit of harmony and cooperation that has come to the two towns. Now that they have stopped their destructive rivalry, the towns have become healthy and prosperous again.

Vocabulary Builder, p. 184

Sample Answers

A. 1. A thunderstorm appears to be imminent, so we have decided to go indoors.

2. Josh made so many errors on the math test that we were distressed at his carelessness.

3. A baby spider monkey is dangling precariously from the top of that tall tree, and we are worried about its safety.

4. The crime was so vile that the judge gave the convicted defendant a long prison sentence.

5. That tiger ate a huge amount of meat! It must have been ravenous.

6. To spurn a fellow guest at a party is not a good way to make a new friend.

B. 1. B; 2. C; 3. B; 4. A

Selection Test A, p. 186

Critical Reading

1. ANS: C   DIF: Easy   OBJ: Comprehension
2. ANS: C   DIF: Easy   OBJ: Interpretation
3. ANS: C   DIF: Easy   OBJ: Literary Analysis
4. ANS: A   DIF: Easy   OBJ: Interpretation
5. ANS: C   DIF: Easy   OBJ: Literary Analysis
6. ANS: A   DIF: Easy   OBJ: Comprehension
7. ANS: C   DIF: Easy   OBJ: Interpretation
8. ANS: C   DIF: Easy   OBJ: Literary Analysis
9. ANS: C   DIF: Easy   OBJ: Literary Analysis
10. ANS: A   DIF: Easy   OBJ: Literary Analysis
11. ANS: D   DIF: Easy   OBJ: Literary Analysis

Vocabulary

12. ANS: B   DIF: Easy   OBJ: Vocabulary
13. ANS: B   DIF: Easy   OBJ: Vocabulary
14. ANS: A   DIF: Easy   OBJ: Vocabulary

Essay

15. Students who choose "The Scarlet Ibis" should discuss the central symbolism of the striking, rare bird, which dies and is then buried by Doodle. The bird's brilliant color and weak condition help convey its remarkable qualities, and these features have parallels in Doodle. In the last scene of the story, the narrator calls Doodle his "fallen scarlet ibis," as he realizes, too late, how much he loved his younger brother. Students who choose "The Golden Kite, the Silver Wind" should discuss the symbolic elements of the allegory. During most of the story, the never-ending competition between the towns is symbolized by the constant rebuilding of their walls. At the end of the story, however, the decision to build walls as a kite and as the wind symbolizes the towns' cooperation and harmony.

    Difficulty: *Easy*

    Objective: *Essay*

16. Students should point out that the narrator in "The Scarlet Ibis" can be affectionate and determined, but he can also be proud and cruel. In "The Golden Kite, the Silver Wind," the Mandarin is excessively proud and envious, and he also has poor judgment. In the first story, the narrator learns to value his little brother, but too late; in the second, the Mandarin changes in time and is able to lead his people out of misery into a condition of cooperation and harmony.

    Difficulty: *Easy*

    Objective: *Essay*

Selection Test B, p. 189

Critical Reading

1. ANS: C   DIF: Average   OBJ: Comprehension
2. ANS: A   DIF: Average   OBJ: Comprehension
3. ANS: D   DIF: Average   OBJ: Interpretation
4. ANS: D   DIF: Average   OBJ: Literary Analysis
5. ANS: C   DIF: Average   OBJ: Interpretation
6. ANS: A   DIF: Average   OBJ: Interpretation
7. ANS: A   DIF: Average   OBJ: Interpretation
8. ANS: D   DIF: Average   OBJ: Comprehension
9. ANS: C   DIF: Average   OBJ: Literary Analysis
10. ANS: D   DIF: Challenging   OBJ: Literary Analysis
11. ANS: C   DIF: Average   OBJ: Interpretation
12. ANS: B   DIF: Average   OBJ: Literary Analysis
13. ANS: A   DIF: Average   OBJ: Literary Analysis

Vocabulary

14. ANS: D   DIF: Average   OBJ: Vocabulary
15. ANS: A   DIF: Challenging   OBJ: Vocabulary
16. ANS: C   DIF: Average   OBJ: Vocabulary
17. ANS: C   DIF: Average   OBJ: Vocabulary

Essay

18. Students should note some of the physical similarities between the bird and Doodle. For example, the ibis is red, and Doodle's skin is described as "red" when he is a baby and blood-stained when his brother finds him dead. The bird's legs are long and thin; Doodle's legs are weak. The bird is weak; Doodle dies from a combination of exhaustion and illness. Students may also note that the scarlet ibis is rare and beautiful; Doodle has proved himself remarkable and rare through his strength and imagination and deep love for his brother.

    Difficulty: *Average*

    Objective: *Essay*

19. Students who select "The Scarlet Ibis" should note that the story is written in a realistic style and that the plot leads up to a tragic ending. The symbols in the story (for example, the time of year, Doodle's coffin, and the scarlet ibis) are filtered through the narrator's poetic sensibility. The total effect of the story is a complex intertwining of love and cruelty, ending with the narrator's intense regret for his brother's death. Students who choose "The Golden Kite, the Silver Wind" should point out that the story is written in the semi-fantastic style of an allegorical fable with some humor and exaggeration. Students may note that the symbol-

ism in the story, arising from the friction between the warring towns, is far less poetic and much more direct than the symbolism in "The Scarlet Ibis."

Difficulty: *Challenging*

Objective: *Essay*

Writing Workshop—Unit 2, Part 2

Review of a Short Story: Integrating Grammar Skills, p. 193

A. 1. grow; 2. thrive; 3. borders; 4. feels

B. 1. Funds for the school system top the list of town expenses.
2. The library and the civic center cost the town little money.
3. Either fees or a special tax funds the local library.
4. Each of the town board members knows the details about the budget.

Spelling Workshop—Unit 2

Tricky or Unusual Consonants, p. 194

A. 1. cologne; 2. overwhelming; 3. adjourn; 4. asthma;
5. condemn; 6. acquaintance; 7. afghan; 8. receipt;
9. ricochet; 10. campaign

B. Sample Answers

1. Before you condemn my campaign for reform, let's discuss the matter. We can adjourn to the library for privacy.
2. I knitted an afghan for my acquaintance. He was allergic to the wool, though, and my gift brought on an overwhelming asthma attack.
3. He did not get a receipt for the cologne, so he will not be able to return it. That is unfortunate because the defective bottle causes cologne to spray in every direction with great force. Droplets that ricochet off the bathroom mirror can seriously sting the eyes.

Unit 2, Part 2 Answers

Benchmark Test 4, p. 197

MULTIPLE CHOICE

1. ANS: C
2. ANS: C
3. ANS: D
4. ANS: D
5. ANS: A
6. ANS: A
7. ANS: B
8. ANS: B
9. ANS: D
10. ANS: A
11. ANS: B
12. ANS: D
13. ANS: D
14. ANS: C
15. ANS: D
16. ANS: A
17. ANS: B
18. ANS: C
19. ANS: D
20. ANS: D
21. ANS: B
22. ANS: C
23. ANS: A
24. ANS: B
25. ANS: D
26. ANS: A
27. ANS: D
28. ANS: D
29. ANS: B
30. ANS: D
31. ANS: C
32. ANS: A
33. ANS: C

ESSAY

34. Students' responses should indicate an understanding of newspaper structure as well as use the correct grammar needed to give advice.
35. Students' letters should be written in the first-person point of view and should and should clearly describe the events in the story.
36. Possible resources include students' personal experiences with natural disasters, the Internet, encyclopedias, and weather videos or DVDs.